FINDING PEACE WITH A DEVASTATING DISEASE

FINDING PEACE WITH A DEVASTATING DISEASE

REFLECTIONS ON ENDOMETRIOSIS

AMY CORFELI

IN SIXTEEN YEARS

ISBN 978-1-7366909-0-1

Cover illustration and design by Hannah Joseph
www.hannahjosephstudio.com

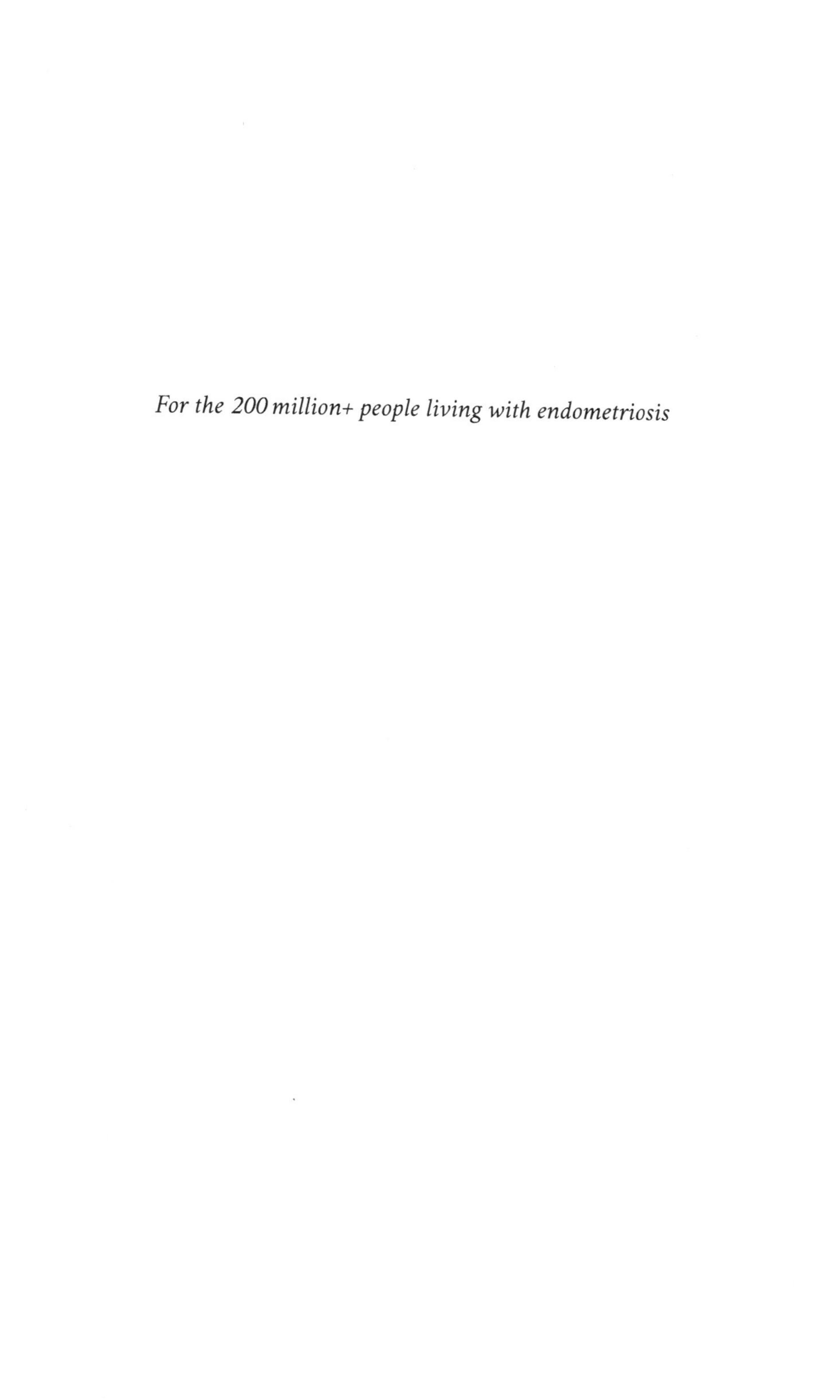

For the 200 million+ people living with endometriosis

DISCLAIMER

This book has content pertaining to physical and mental health issues. Nothing in this book is intended to be a substitute for the professional medical advice, diagnosis, or treatment provided by a medical professional or mental health professional. I am not a medical professional nor a mental health professional. This book and the self-reflection prompts for the reader's participation is not meant to diagnose, treat, or cure any physical, mental or emotional issue, disease, or condition. You agree and acknowledge that I am not providing medical advice or mental health advice in any way.

If you have or suspect you have a medical condition or mental health condition, always consult a qualified medical professional or mental health professional.

This is a collection of my personal reflections on illness and healing with optional self-reflection prompts for you to engage with. In the reflections that have longer descriptions about pain, I have included a note at the beginning advising the reader. However, since this book is about the realities of living with endometriosis, there are descriptions of pain, symptoms, and mental health issues weaved into many of the reflections throughout the book, including those that have no advisory note at the beginning. Stop here and do not move forward with reading this book if you may not be comfortable with reading about these topics. If you do choose to read this book and/or engage with the self-reflection prompts, and you feel uncomfortable, triggered, or upset during the reading or use of this book, you may want to stop reading/engaging with this book and/or immediately seek the support of a loved one or a mental health professional.

You agree that I will not be liable to you, or to any other individual, company, or entity, for any type of damages, injury, or harm, including direct, indirect, physical, mental, emotional or spiritual in connection to this book.

If you do not agree to this disclaimer, stop here, and do not read or engage with any part of this book.

CONTENTS

HOW TO READ THIS BOOK

Self-Reflection Prompts

This book is composed of seventy-six of my reflections on various topics such as mindfulness, meaning, and acceptance. At the end of each essay, I have provided a Self-Reflection Prompt with questions unique to that topic.

These prompts offer a chance to explore what these topics mean for *you* in relation to your own illness and experiences. If you don't have endometriosis, substitute that reference in the reflections for your own illness or a challenge you are facing. Each individual prompt is optional. If you choose to engage with them and feel uncomfortable, triggered, or upset by one of the prompts, you may want to skip that particular one and/or immediately seek the support of a loved one or a mental health professional.

Writing

The best way to explore the prompts is by sitting down to free write with a pen and paper or on your computer. Set a timer for fifteen minutes and just write whatever comes to mind. This might sound tedious, but by writing, we can organize a flood of thoughts and feelings into something coherent. Often thoughts race through our mind and are too all over the place to allow us to find that depth in ourselves or any emotional breakthroughs. Writing can be transformative and help us find our deep truths under the superficial ones. It can also help us with lowering stress or anxiety levels, or even just feeling like we've been heard. For many, writing is a safe space to express themselves openly and without judgment.

Important: When you finish, you can immediately delete the document or shred the paper—there is no need to keep it, share it, or reread it unless you want to.

Find a time when you won't be interrupted and where you have privacy. This way, you are able to openly explore your experiences and feelings. Don't worry if what you write isn't 'nice'; don't worry if you are repeating yourself or complaining. Don't worry about spelling, grammar, or sloppy handwriting. Just get it out! When we truly express ourselves, many of our uncomfortable feelings and experiences lose power over us.

If you can't think of what to write, then write whatever comes to mind, like "I have nothing to say on this. I can't think of what to write. This exercise feels useless. Has fifteen minutes gone by yet?" Just write whatever comes until the timer goes off. With practice, it usually gets easier to free write. On the other hand, if the timer goes off and you aren't finished writing, keep going until you're done!

I'm excited for you to see where your self-reflections can take you. If you choose not to do the self-reflections, you can always come back to them at any time.

Sending you support and strength. May you find what you are looking for.

INTRODUCTION TO ENDOMETRIOSIS

While many people reading this book may have endometriosis themselves, some may not. If you are unfamiliar with endometriosis, knowing what it is will help you relate to my experiences in the book, which are common among many people with endometriosis.

What is Endometriosis?

One in ten people assigned female at birth have endometriosis, which comes to about 200 million people worldwide living with this disease. In spite of its prevalence, there is often a long delay in diagnosis. Various studies have shown that the average time to be diagnosed is between 4-11 years.

Endometriosis is when tissue *similar* to the endometrium (the uterine lining) grows in the body. This tissue is not supposed to be there and may grow on the ovaries, pelvic side-walls, bowel, bladder, lungs, diaphragm, or other parts of the body. Endometriosis is made of glands and stroma; these glands secrete an inflammatory substance which can irritate the surrounding tissue and destabilize nearby capillaries, causing bleeding in the surrounding tissues. This bleeding and inflammation can cause an immune response, the formation of scar tissue and adhesions, new blood vessels to grow in surrounding tissue (angiogenesis), and pain.

Endometriosis can cause high levels of inflammation in the body, organs to fuse together (for example, the bowel fuses to the uterus or ovaries fuse to the pelvic wall), bowel blockages, lung collapses, an upregulation of the central nervous system (causing a person to feel more pain to less stimuli), and other serious health problems. Symptoms may include (but aren't limited to) debilitating menstrual pain, pain away from the menstrual cycle (which may be acute or chronic), painful sex, painful bowel movements, painful urination, pain with use of a tampon, leg pain, back pain, shoulder pain, chest pain, pain when breathing, digestive problems like diarrhea or constipation, bloating, food intolerances, infertility, brain fog, fatigue, and more.

In many parts of this book, I refer to the agonizing, debilitating, and relentless pain I experience due to endometriosis. This is no exaggeration. In 2018, the UK's National Health Service named endometriosis in a list of twenty of the most painful conditions a person can get.[1] It was validating to see endometriosis get the awareness it deserves and unsurprising to those of us who suffer from its ruthless pain.

Endometriosis Treatments

In a few parts of the book, I mention conversations with my doctors about treatment. Unfortunately, due to the perpetuation of myths and misinformation, many gynecologists who are not experts in endometriosis offer the patient a hysterectomy as a cure for endometriosis. However, this does not cure endometriosis (endometriosis has no cure) and if endometriosis lesions aren't removed during that surgery, then endometriosis symptoms and pain can persist.

Additionally, GnRh drugs that medically induce menopause, as well as birth controls, only manage the *symptoms* of endometriosis. Although these may be prescribed as 'treatment' for the disease,[2] hormonal therapy doesn't remove endometriosis. Endometriosis can also still progress while a person is on hormonal therapy.

The 'gold standard treatment' for endometriosis is excision surgery because it removes the disease at the *root*. This is different from the ablation of endometriosis, which is a surgical technique that burns the endometriosis *superficially*. (Many people may have heard of endometrial ablation, but to clarify, ablation of *endometriosis* and *endometrial* ablation are completely different. Endometrial ablation is when the uterine lining is removed to stop or lessen menstrual bleeding.)

Excision surgery is renowned in the field as being an extremely difficult gynecological surgery; it requires a high skill level to remove endometriosis from delicate tissues, as well as to separate organs that may have fused together due to adhesions. The majority of gynecologists do endometriosis ablation surgery, not excision. In 2020, it was estimated that there are only about 200 skilled excision specialists in the United States. Unfortunately, there are many barriers to access an excision specialist, such as insurance hurdles, cost, location, and even lack of referrals to a specialist due to inadequate education among gynecologists (who may instead prescribe one of the other aforementioned 'treatments'). Therefore, the 'gold standard treatment' of excision remains a privilege that only some people can access instead of being the standard endometriosis treatment that everyone can access.

Because endometriosis is a complex inflammatory condition that can affect the full body, it's recommended that the patient work with a multidisciplinary team with excision at the cornerstone to address the disease from a full-body approach. Additionally, endometriosis may be present with other common co-conditions like Interstitial Cystitis/Painful Bladder Syndrome, pelvic floor dysfunction, small intestinal bacterial overgrowth (SIBO), gut dysbiosis, hormone imbalance, or irritable bowel syndrome (IBS). While many people do have significant improvement in their quality of life after excision surgery, others may need to address co-conditions and secondary pain generators to see more relief.

Endometriosis Resources

This disease is mired in misinformation and outdated myths, which are even perpetuated from doctors and well-meaning endometriosis advocates. It's vital to learn about the disease from trusted sources that give accurate information. I provide a list of helpful resources for people with endometriosis on my website at https://insixteenyears.com/.

MY ENDOMETRIOSIS STORY

This book is an exploration of finding peace with endometriosis and what it means to heal on multiple levels. I thought you might find it helpful to have some background knowledge of my endometriosis story.

For many years, my symptoms consumed me. My senior year of high school was spent running to the toilet with relentless diarrhea, sometimes up to twenty-five times a day. I was afraid to eat or leave the house—what if there was no bathroom around when the urge to go undoubtedly hit?

In college, the leg pain started and didn't stop for over seven years. The nausea was so intense in the mornings that I had to switch to afternoon classes. The fatigue overpowered me. I could barely keep my eyes open, took several naps each day, and couldn't walk up a flight of stairs.

My period was terrifying. From the very start, menstruation came with out-of-this-world pain. One of the first times my period came, my mom called an ambulance because I had collapsed on the floor, vomiting and moaning in agony. I tried many different prescription and non-prescription medications, but nothing touched the pain except prescription Naproxen.

Even then, it didn't completely eliminate my pain but only took the edge off, so I literally planned my life around my period because I was incapacitated during those days.

Those months of hell turned into years. Yet despite the severe symptoms, no doctor could find anything wrong with me. Within the first two years of getting sick, I saw eleven different doctors. Two colonoscopies, an upper endoscopy, an exploratory laparoscopy, ultrasounds, neurological tests, allergy tests, stool samples, and blood work all showed that I was in 'excellent' health. Two misinformed doctors even told me that I didn't have endometriosis.

It took sixteen years, but I was finally diagnosed with endometriosis. That's when I learned that the majority of gynecologists don't have adequate training in the disease. They may not recognize the suggestion of its presence on scans such as ultrasounds or MRIs. Or they may not know that not all types of endometriosis show up on these scans, and therefore a negative scan doesn't necessarily mean the patient doesn't have endometriosis. Laparoscopy with a pathology report is the only way to have a definitive diagnosis of endometriosis, but many gynecologists who are not skilled in recognizing the various appearances or locations of endometriosis miss obvious signs of the disease. I didn't know any of this back then, so when one gynecologist told me I didn't have endometriosis after performing an ultrasound, and another told me I didn't have it after doing an exploratory laparoscopy, I believed that endometriosis wasn't the cause of my symptoms. After all, these two doctors had told me that I didn't have it.

So, for years I thought—in spite of my debilitating menstrual pain and all my other symptoms—that I had nothing wrong with me. After all, that's what I'd been told by every doctor I saw. In fact, I had been told by several gynecologists that period pain was normal, that symptoms like mine tended to be psychosomatic, and I'd been referred more than once to a psychiatrist.

After my endometriosis diagnosis, I learned that my experience with doctors dismissing my symptoms, as well as the years-long delay in diagnosis, is common among people with endometriosis.

Managing Symptoms

Two years after my symptoms began, in 2004, when I was nineteen, I stumbled upon two books about healing fatigue through eating an anti-inflammatory diet. In complete desperation, I decided to try it. Within a few weeks, my relentless diarrhea improved. There was nothing more motivating than seeing this symptom lessen after two years of trying various medicines for it with no avail! I committed to eating this way 100%. Amazingly, within a few months, the chronic pelvic pain unexpectedly disappeared. I also started to get my energy back, and the heavy blanket of fatigue lifted from me.

Through those books, the door to feeling better opened up for me. They were my first introduction to taking control of my health. Until then, I had no idea that the way I lived and what I ate could impact the way I felt. I spent the next decade obsessed with researching, reading, and educating myself on the body, learning how it's a complex system influenced by a multitude of factors, like food choices, sleep habits, environmental toxins, and even thought patterns. After years of trial and error, I found a combination of diet and lifestyle habits that helped improve my quality of life. By my mid-twenties, although I still had a full array of symptoms (diarrhea, digestive problems, severe bloating, leg pain, nausea, fatigue, and excruciating periods), they were better managed, which enabled me to start working full time—something that wasn't possible for so many years when my symptoms controlled my life! However, feeling halfway decent was extremely dependent on how I lived. If I strayed from the anti-inflammatory diet at all, got too stressed, didn't get enough sleep, or any other number of situations, my symptoms would immediately flare.

Nothing I tried ever helped the brutal period cramps; in fact, they only worsened as the years passed. Around thirty years old, that same soul-wrenching pain started to appear in my life away from my period: when I ate starchy or fibrous foods, drank something cold, sneezed, had sex, drove over a speed bump, or had a bowel movement.

Diagnosis

Once again, I desperately went to multiple gynecologists, but they didn't know how to help or only half listened and recommended birth control. The fourth one finally said she suspected I had endometriosis and suggested I get a hysterectomy or take medications (with potentially serious side effects) to temporarily go into medical menopause. Before making that decision, I realized I need to learn more about endometriosis. Finding information about the disease was much easier in 2017 than it had been 2004, thanks to podcasts, websites, and social media that didn't exist when I was younger. I learned the importance of seeing an excision specialist[1], and to my incredible good fortune and luck, one was located in my city and was in-network with my insurance provider. Some months later, I had an appointment with him. The ultrasound he did showed a grapefruit-sized mass on my left ovary, along with a few cysts and a rotated uterus. When my bloodwork came back elevated for cancer markers, I was referred to a gynecologic oncology surgeon. Two weeks later, he operated on me to remove the twelve centimeter mass, as well as my ovary. The biopsy showed that it wasn't cancer but rather a twelve centimeter endometrioma. I was finally diagnosed with stage IV endometriosis at thirty-three years old, giving a name to a disease that had gone undiagnosed for more than half of my life.

Excision Surgery

Four months later, just when I had recovered from the first surgery, I had excision surgery for endometriosis with the original excision surgeon. I had bowel (both small and large) and bladder involvement, and an obliterated cul-de-sac (my intestines were fused to my uterus). My sigmoid colon was narrowed to a third of its width and partially obstructed. The excision surgeon told me in the post-op appointment: "I have no idea how you were using the bathroom."

I will never forget those words. After sixteen years of struggling to be diagnosed, believed, and heard, those words—along with the shocking surgery pictures—were proof that I was truly sick. I was infuriated that my very real, serious disease hadn't been diagnosed earlier, which had led to sixteen years of suffering. It is heartbreaking to me that from such a young age, we go through so many trials and tribulations because we are fighting not only against endometriosis, but against a system of misinformation, dismissive doctors, and lack of access to expert care, all while battling the pain, fatigue, nausea, doubt, and more.

Since excision, my endometriosis symptoms have improved considerably. The surgeon was able to get about 95% of my endometriosis, with the exception of the endometriosis in my rectum. I no longer have excruciating pain during sex, bowel movements, or my period, and not a day goes by when I don't give thanks for this and for my ability to have had access to excision. However, I still deal with fibromyalgia pain; bladder pain, urgency, and frequency from interstitial cystitis; heavy bleeding, fatigue, and dizziness during my periods; racing heart, insomnia, migraines, hives, and anaphylaxis from histamine intolerance and possible Mast Cell Activation Syndrome (which is a new condition that began after the excision surgery); low hormone output, which causes hot flashes, insomnia, and irregular periods (also new since excision); and food intolerances, bloating, and digestive problems from small intestinal bacterial overgrowth (SIBO). While excision surgery has been a privilege that has helped me immensely, I am far from feeling fully better and now trying to tackle all of my co-conditions, many of which are related directly or indirectly to endometriosis. I'm still juggling the doctor's appointments, the financial strain, and the overwhelm of trying to take care of myself, work, and live in this hectic, modern world.

Searching for Peace

When I was twenty-six (and still undiagnosed), I began exploring the concepts of healing, acceptance, and mindfulness as a way to figure out how to cope with these symptoms that were ravaging my life. At that time, I moved to Japan to teach English, for the adventure, the split shift job which enabled me to nap at midday, and because living abroad gave me the opportunity to more easily have the lifestyle I needed—walking and movement built into my day, an abundance of fresh vegetables and fish, less processed foods—than I could have in the United States. In Japan, I began attending meditation retreats, reading heavily into ancient wisdom teachings, and surrounding myself with people who valued introspection, mindfulness, and gratitude.

After four years in Japan, I spent a year volunteering as a teacher in Achuar territory. The Achuar are a group of Jivaroan people native to the Amazonian regions either side of the Ecuador and Peru border. I lived in a village of 150 people, deep in the Amazon rainforest. It was the most beautiful, and perhaps most important, year of my life. Once more, the food and lifestyle that I was naturally surrounded by was fantastic for managing flares. On an emotional level, living in such a stress-free environment, in a simple cabin among the natural elements where time doesn't suffocate one as it does in our Western culture, I spent a lot of time meditating and reflecting on what's important to me.

Most of the writings in this book are from my years in Japan and the Amazon, which occurred *before* being diagnosed with endometriosis. I didn't receive my diagnosis until I had surgery to remove the endometrioma at thirty-three years old, sixteen years after the first onset of my symptoms! That is why the story of my diagnosis and surgery are toward the end of the book. However, for consistency, I refer to my pain and symptoms throughout the book as endometriosis, since that's what it always was—even when I didn't know its name at that time.

Looking for peace with endometriosis has had a ripple effect on all aspects of my life. I now have less anxiety about uncertainty, more confidence in my ability to handle challenges, and a deeper understanding of myself. I've been able to heal many of my past emotional hurts and traumas that were both related and unrelated to my illness; I've been able to change the way I feel about myself and my life. I began my journey with acceptance to try to cope with the pain that had been consuming my life for over a decade, but it turns out the skills and perspective I've been gaining have been incredibly useful for facing the myriad of challenges life brings, everything from financial insecurity, to loss, to a global pandemic.

IS ENDOMETRIOSIS A 'DEVASTATING DISEASE'?

Note: This essay contains descriptions of symptoms that some readers may find upsetting.

When I was working on the title of this book, many of the people I showed it to that do not have endometriosis doubted my decision to call endometriosis a 'devastating disease'. On the other hand, the people that *do* have endometriosis nodded in agreement at this adjective because that is their lived experience.

Endometriosis is a misunderstood disease, and the information that is available is often rampant with errors and misinformation. Endometriosis isn't 'just a bad period' or 'brutal menstrual cramps.' While many people do have incapacitating pain during their periods, myself included, endometriosis is a full-body disease that can affect every single aspect of our lives.

The following is a raw, unexaggerated account of what it's like (for me) to live with endometriosis. This is included here at the beginning of the book in an effort to increase awareness regarding the seriousness of this incurable disease that affects one in ten people assigned female at birth.

While all of us have a different experience with endometriosis, if you are reading this book as a person also living with endometriosis, I'm sure you can relate. I'm also sure that there is so much more we could collectively say about the devastation of this disease and that my description doesn't do justice to all of the ways endometriosis can ravage our bodies and our lives.

If you are reading this book as a person who is trying to better understand endometriosis and how it affects a person you care for, my hope is that this description will offer you a glimpse of what they are living with.

What is it like to live with endometriosis?

Endometriosis is traumatic. It's lonely. It's devastating. It crushes your soul and fills you with despair. It's being terrified to have sex, drive over a speedbump, or drink water on an empty stomach for fear of triggering incapacitating pain that makes you vomit, writhe on the floor, and beg the universe for the pain to stop. It's lying in your own vomit in bed, still puking and too debilitated by searing pain to roll over, let alone get to the toilet or clean up.

Endometriosis is not sharing any intimacy with your partner because not only does sex cause hours or even days of raging cramps, but any kind of physical touch is excruciating due to central sensitization after years of living in chronic pain. It's broken relationships and broken marriages because dealing with constant pain, infertility, medical debt, and last minute cancellation of plans due to a flare can put extra strain on a relationship. *Not* because we are a burden or unlovable as people with a chronic illness—we are neither—but because relationships are already hard work, and an illness that is difficult to understand and live with can add new layers to that, exacerbating problems that couples already had.

Endometriosis is broken dreams, unstarted careers, and abandoned hobbies because we are too sick to leave our beds, let alone pursue any of our interests. It's isolation, fear, depression, anxiety, overwhelm, anger, bitterness, trauma, PTSD, and the psychological toll that living with symptoms 24/7 and feeling unsafe in your own body can cause.

Endometriosis is not eating so that you can leave the house without fear of having diarrhea in public or on yourself. It's having to cook every single one of your meals because you're unable to eat more than just a few plain foods due to your severe food intolerances. It's feeling deprived, restricted, and frustrated that you can't enjoy eating at birthday parties, celebrations, and holiday gatherings, trying not to be jealous that everyone else so casually can. It's being constantly terrified to eat anything because you are scared of the pain food causes—it ripping through your intestines, your body rebelling and spending hours on the toilet with diarrhea. Or conversely, the food doesn't move at all and sits in your intestines like a rock.

Endometriosis is having multiple surgeries, related complications, and recoveries so difficult that your family has to wash your body in the shower because you are unable to wash yourself. It's having cancer scares when endometriosis nodules appear on MRI scans and then subsequent blood tests show indications of cancer markers (due to endometriosis). It's eyes closing mid-sentence from fatigue and passing out within minutes of beginning any kind of exertion—like going to the grocery store or running errands.

Endometriosis is wondering in your senior year of high school when the doctor will figure out what is wrong with you instead of wondering when you will have your first kiss and what you will wear to prom. Wondering if you will *ever* feel better or if your life is going to be this overwhelming onslaught of symptoms forever. It's having over fifty doctor's appointments in one year while juggling chronic pain, somehow getting to class or dragging yourself to your job every single day, and managing the endless work of taking care of yourself.

Endometriosis is having to retrain your bladder, wear adult diapers, and poop and pee behind bushes and in bags in your car because your organs have become dysfunctional. It's losing organs in surgery, losing the ability to have a biological child, and even pushing aside the idea of adoption—how could you take care of another human being when you are weighed down by the burden of taking care of yourself? It's people congratulating you on being pregnant, when you're actually infertile and your giant belly is just a bloated marker of the disease that festers inside.

Endometriosis is getting spontaneous excruciating pain because of an unexpected trigger, causing you to pass out on the bathroom floor at your workplace or keel over on a subway platform in absolute agony. It's 'causing a scene'—everyone staring at you, pointing, whispering, making comments, and accusing you of exaggerating, as the pain tears apart your insides and rips out your soul.

Endometriosis is being unable to concentrate or sleep due to the pain in your legs, hips, back, joints, arms, fingers, uterus, intestines, bladder, rectum, and vagina. It's being afraid all the time. Being exhausted all the time. Being told by the doctors who should be helping you that none of it is real, that it's psychosomatic, that you're seeking drugs, that it's 'normal' for womxn[1] to have pain, that managing stress or seeing a psychologist would help you realize 'it's in your head'—instead of addressing your very real and serious endometriosis. It's being told by coworkers and friends not to talk about your bodily issues because it's socially inappropriate. It's being called gross, disgusting, and dirty after having bled through a menstrual product onto your pants or experiencing incontinence in front of someone.

Endometriosis is getting countless tests repeated by different doctors and being told you're fine: colonoscopies, ultrasounds, stool analyses, neurological examinations, and blood tests. It's not getting diagnosed for sixteen years, even though your symptoms are severe, because over forty doctors either don't believe you or just can't figure out what's wrong with you. It's numerous surgeries and dealing with side effects from hormonal treatments such as overpowering fatigue, migraines, and changes to mental health—while far too young.

Endometriosis is seeing an incorrect definition of your disease on medical websites and having doctors and everyone around you recommending inaccurate 'treatments' for the disease. It's hearing from your misinformed gynecologist that the only cure is to remove important organs like the uterus, but in reality this is *not* a cure. Or being recommended by your gynecologist to take X medication as 'the only option for endometriosis', only to have an actual endometriosis specialist tell you it's *not* the only option and it may even cause permanent side effects—but you weren't ever informed of this medication's side effects. It's being told by people that you meet, in utmost seriousness and in an honest desire to help, to stop having sex with demons or that some trendy body detoxification or juicing routine will cure you.

Endometriosis is knowing that there is no cure to this disease and having to shoulder that heavy reality every single day.

Endometriosis is living with all of this for decades with no end in sight, and this could have begun when you were a teenager or even a child.

This is endometriosis, and it is, without a doubt, devastating for the millions of people who live with it every single day.

FINDING PEACE WITH A DEVASTATING DISEASE

1

CAN I RECLAIM MY LIFE FROM ENDOMETRIOSIS?

Sometimes, I feel that endometriosis has robbed me of my life.

For years, it's been one miserable blur. Last week, I was bedridden several days because of my period; yesterday, I canceled my plans because I was so fatigued; today, it's nausea; tomorrow, my day will probably be disrupted by diarrhea; next week, another trip to the ER. It feels like there is no break from always being sick.

My life has bounced from one symptom to another for the past decade, and I have felt depressed more often than not. Eating, sleeping, using the bathroom, sex, just being alive—it's all pain, all the time.

Until very recently, that is. I've been learning about mindfulness: the practice of bringing your awareness to the present moment, and doing so without judging the experience, feelings, sensations, or thoughts that are present. It's simple yet beautiful, and to me, somehow liberating. Mindfulness is teaching me to be more awake—more conscious—to what's around me, as opposed to being lost in my thoughts or the stories I tell myself. For example, instead of sitting outside thinking about all the chores that have piled up because I've been too sick to do them, I just take a moment to really breathe the outside air and feel the breeze on my face. When I manage to do that—to be fully present with myself, paying attention to where I am right now —I can see that there *are* some moments of beauty and meaning among the countless moments of pain.

For years I have been unaware of this truth, too exhausted to see past the pain, and too angry at life to let go of the hate and rage I have toward this disease. Take this one time about ten years ago. In my early twenties, my body hurt nonstop, especially in my legs and joints. This made it extremely difficult to sleep. Every night, I would toss and turn for hours in bed until finally falling asleep exhausted. When the alarm went off, I would wake up and instantly feel the pain. I would leap out of bed, desperate to stretch my body and relieve the stiffness.

My partner at that time loved to cuddle, but I never wanted to. He wanted to lounge in bed together, to wake up and hold each other like couples in movies do, but that was impossible for me. When he touched my arm, my back, my hands—it all hurt, so we never relaxed in bed together in the morning. As soon as I woke up, I'd rush out of the bed as if it were on fire.

Then, there was one single special morning when I woke up and I wasn't in pain. None at all.

It was a miracle.

We finally got to cuddle, but instead of being happy, I was heartbroken. Instead of concentrating on how we were enjoying this beautiful moment together, all I could think about was how unfair it was that we couldn't do this all the time. Although I was there physically, I wasn't *really* there. I was off in my head, obsessing, lamenting, wishing, wanting, and feeling furious that endometriosis had stolen so many of these moments from me. Thoughts were running through my head like, "I should be able to do this everyday. This isn't fair. Endo has robbed me of so much. Why does my body never cooperate? I hate this disease!"

I was so lost in my angry thoughts that I didn't actually enjoy our cuddling. I ended up missing the beauty of this precious, pain-free moment with the person that I loved.

Looking back over the years, I see now that this has happened over and over. I have so frequently been emotionally absent from the present moment—present moments that, at times, were filled with joy.

For years, I've complained that being sick is stealing my life from me, but is it just the disease? I finally recognize that *I* am also stealing my life. Even on rare days that I wasn't sick, I made my way mindlessly, not paying attention to my experiences or the people I was with. I've always complained about how I've watched everyone around me getting jobs, choosing college majors, going on dates, and enjoying themselves while I have been stuck in bed or on the toilet. But I've failed to recognize that I, too, have chosen a major, gone on dates, and had fun—I just spent so much time thinking only about the pain and frustration of my disease that those moments flew by me. Yes, I've had many unbearable moments, but I've also traveled and loved and laughed so hard that I cried.

It's not that my life has been lacking in happy, meaningful moments. They have been there all along, but for years I've been oblivious to them. I've been living in my head, focused on my thoughts of how my life should be instead of participating fully in the actual life before me.

Endometriosis is chronic. It's forever. It's with me, and it will be with me, every single day. But by being aware of the present, I can see that life provides me with tiny moments of relief from my illness. Yesterday evening, as I was making my dinner, I noticed that for several minutes while chopping vegetables, I didn't experience any symptoms. It was like my illness didn't exist. I didn't feel sick—I just felt calm, touching the thick wood cutting board under my hand, enjoying the rhythmic motion of the knife, listening to the sound of the stirfry sizzling on the stove. I was just a person, standing at her kitchen counter, preparing a meal for herself. It was so normal and so wonderful —and I could have missed that moment if I had been mindlessly lost in my thoughts about "will this make me sick later?" or rushing to finish cooking.

Mindfulness and gratitude seem to go hand in hand. When I'm not present to each moment, it's hard to notice the good parts of life, and it's hard to be grateful when I don't notice the good. With presence, I can appreciate little things like taking a shower, getting the mail, or eating an apple. On days I'm especially sick, routine tasks can become monumental challenges, and something as simple as brushing my teeth feels like a feat of heroic strength and determination. If I pay attention, I can find many moments—even these seemingly mundane ones—to be celebrated, little gems in the sandbox of life to be appreciated and collected.

As I practice mindfulness, the world is beginning to feel differently than it did. I'm still sick, but life has more beauty in it, more meaning, more moments of joy. And who doesn't want that?

Self-Reflection

Have you been missing your life by not paying attention to the present moment? Do you often find your mind wandering to the past or the future? This could be worrying, planning, dwelling on something, reliving something, or any other way your mind leaves the present moment to think about something that isn't happening right now.

A good way to be in the present is to use your five senses. Let's practice for a few minutes. What can you hear at this moment? Take a minute to just listen. Notice any sounds, loud or soft, close or far, without judging them.

Now, spend a minute really looking around you and taking

in what you see. It's easy to quickly glance around, but really look around and try to notice what you can. What is in front of you? What colors are there? Is the lighting bright or dim?

Next, take a deep breath in. Can you smell anything? What about sensations? If you're sitting, take a minute to sink into the chair and really feel the weight of your body pressing against it. Can you feel the air on your skin or your clothes? Are you hot, warm, comfortable, cold?

Allow yourself to spend a minute with this moment, right now, without wishing it were over or judging it as good or bad or boring. If you find thoughts creeping in, that's okay—don't judge them, and don't judge yourself for having them. Instead, when you notice you are distracted, bring your attention back to what's right here in front of you.

After another minute or two, write about everything you saw, heard, smelled, and felt in as much detail as possible.

2

IT'S LIKE BEING UPSET THE SKY IS BLUE

If I looked outside every day hoping to see a green sky, I'd be disappointed. If I *really* wanted a green sky, I'd probably be frustrated or sad too. If I felt that the sky *must* be green, I might even throw rocks at it while screaming, "Why aren't you green?!" I would tell everyone around me that I hate the sky because it shouldn't be this way—it *should* be green.

It would be exhausting to hate the fact that the sky is blue. I'd use so much energy resisting this truth—a truth that might be unwanted to me but is the way things are nonetheless.

Why should the color of the sky influence my happiness? Luckily, it doesn't. But what does influence my happiness is my anger and injustice toward having endometriosis. Is a painful, incurable illness anything like the blue sky? If I actually did want the sky to be green, then yes, they would have something in common: I cannot change their existence and abhor them both just for what they are. And they would both have power over me, invoking a slew of painful emotions and reactions since they defy what I think reality should be.

As much as I don't want endometriosis, as unfair as it seems —it's a part of my life now. The more I argue with my illness, reject the idea of it, and fight against it, the more it drains me. Why do I do this? It's like I'm waiting to no longer have endometriosis so I can go *back* to my life. Yet there is no going back; there is only going forward. So how do I want to move forward? Instead of waiting for a 'better' life, waiting for things to go my way, waiting for the sky to be another color, I instead need to figure out how to live well *with* this illness. How can I be okay with this reality, even if it cannot change?

There's no doubt that many aspects of having endometriosis are devastating. It's ravaged my career, my fertility, my relationships, my basic body functions (eating, peeing, pooping, sleeping, menstruating), my ability to be at ease in my own body. It would be a lie to pretend that endometriosis isn't upsetting. It *is* upsetting, and it's understandable why I've been so infuriated and full of grief. These feelings are valid, and I shouldn't push them away. But I've been living from them for a decade now, and I no longer want endometriosis to have power over me. This disease has taken away so much from me—I no longer want to give it agency over the way I feel. I want that freedom over my happiness. That is why I really want to find peace with endometriosis.

I've read memoirs of people from all over the world who manage to find peace with the most awful situations: disease, death, poverty, loss. Seeing that millions of humans throughout history have used 'acceptance' to find solace in their fate shows me that peace with endometriosis *is* possible. But *how* did they find peace with such difficult circumstances? Will *I* be able to find peace with my body and my health? Where do I even start? I don't know, but there has to be something more for me than living from anger and sadness. I suppose right now the first, and perhaps most important, step I can take is to believe in the possibility that one day I, too, will be able to find peace with my life exactly how it is.

Self-Reflection

- What emotions do the words 'I have endometriosis' bring up in you? (If you don't have endometriosis, fill in your own illness or problem that you are facing.)
- Do you have any physical reactions in your body to those words? For example, does your stomach tighten, your breath go shallow, or your energy drain?
- Now, what emotions come up in you when you think about the sky being blue? What about thinking about how fish need water to survive?
- What else do you accept without thinking twice about it?
- Do you think you are capable of one day finding this same acceptance toward endometriosis?
- Do you want to?
- Even if you don't know *how* to find it right now, do you believe it's possible? Why or why not?

3

THE RAGING FIRE

Note: This essay contains descriptions of pain that some readers may find upsetting.

I'm trapped inside of a room that's on fire. The flames are coming toward me, slowly and inevitably, and all I can do is curl up in a ball on the floor and cover my face.

Panic rises in me as I watch the flames approach me. How do I breathe as the smoke starts to choke me?

This is what my endometriosis pain feels like to me. It's full of desperation and fear. It has an aura of loneliness; it stinks of sweat and vomit.

The pain isn't localized to my abdomen, although it originates there, the catalyst for the inferno. The pain is now its own entity, agonizing and uncontrollable. It radiates out of my body, taking on a much bigger dimension, filling the room, raging without mercy, and consuming me.

The fire has reached me, and it's unbearable. All my movement is frantic. My hands squeeze in and out of fists. Sometimes I hyperventilate. Other times, I find myself holding my breath. For almost three hours, I vomit and have diarrhea over two dozen times. An incredible array of moans, sobs, and screams come out of my mouth. It's startling, even to me, but somehow letting myself express the pain without holding back makes it more emotionally bearable.

I have survived my period over and over, but it never gets easier. I feel a deep fear in my gut. I'm desperate. It's been hours. Hours! This flare is long, too long; the seconds tick by slowly, too slowly, measured by my tears and moans of agony. Will this pain ever stop?

"I can't do this anymore. Please, please," I beg out loud, choking on my words and gasping for breath. There is no air left in this room. It has all been devoured by the pain.

I'm not going to die. I know that. I have lived through at least a hundred experiences like this. Hours of pain that no medicine could ease and yet somehow I've always survived. Not, of course, without some consequences: PTSD and nightmares, too many unpaid days from work, broken relationships. Romantic partners and roommates never last long. It always ends up being too much for them to stand around helplessly while I wail in pain every single month. I can understand how it's disturbing for them—it's something that I've never gotten used to either.

"I can't do this! I can't do this!" I howl over and over, "Please help me." I beg the universe while curled up on the floor in a ball. Five seconds later, I'm heaving over the toilet. "Please, please help me."

Nothing cares. The bedroom chair doesn't move. The paintings hang on the wall, staring stubbornly back at me. The pillows lie tranquilly on the bed. I am alone. I am so incredibly alone. I begin to feel desperate. I need someone else to be there with me, to tell me that I will make it. I don't know if I'm going to make it. I'm not going to make it. This pain is not going to stop.

I grab my phone and call my best friend. When she picks up,

I can't even manage a hello. My throat burns from throwing up; my mouth is as dry as cardboard. "Tell me I can do this," I sob, whimper, gasp into the phone. "Tell me it's ending. Please."

I just need reassurance. Support. To know that someone else is out there, knowing what's going on for me right now—knowing that I'm in hell, knowing that I need help.

Her voice is calm and soothing. She is there for me. She cares. "You are going to survive this. You have already survived this, dozens of times. You are stronger than the pain. You are already doing this, and you are almost done."

"Ok," I whisper.

"You can make it through," she says. "Listen to my voice. *You can make it.*"

I can make it. I can do this. I just have to stay strong and wait until the fire burns itself out; the pain will fade and the smoke will clear. Eventually, the room will fill with air again, and then I can pull myself up from the ashes and finally breathe.

Self-Reflection

- How would you describe your endometriosis pain? If it is too difficult or traumatic to describe the pain, try describing a symptom that has less of an emotional effect on you. For example, describe your nausea, your fatigue, your leg pain, or your stomachache. Use as many details as you can, as if you were explaining the pain/symptom to a loved one who has never experienced it.
- Where is the pain/symptom in your body?
- What sensations does it bring? It is crushing, burning, clawing?
- Is it all-consuming, draining, overwhelming?

4

CHRONIC MEANS FOREVER

A memory from high school.

The doctor came out and introduced himself, a man who barely shook my hand. Right away, I didn't like him. How could I, when he had a handshake like that? That day, everything really unsettled me: the elderly in the waiting room, the pale green color of the walls, his dismissive handshake. All I wanted to do was wake up from this bad dream.

He was a gastrointestinal doctor. Hopefully, he was going to figure out why I had been having diarrhea for the past several weeks and why my abdomen was so bloated that I looked pregnant.

Sitting in that doctor's office was the first time I had really contemplated the thought of having a chronic illness. Chronic—as in, the rest of my life. As soon as my mom and I had walked into the waiting room, I became aware of the gravity of this. Every patient there was over sixty. *I shouldn't be here,* I thought. *I'm only seventeen.*

Just the thought of having a disease at such a young age made me want to throw up. The fear I felt in the pit of my stomach overpowered me, and I found it hard to breathe. It had only been a month of feeling ill, and I was already falling apart. What would I do if this feeling of sickness *never* went away?

When the doctor called me in for the tests, I forced myself to lie still on an X-ray machine, trying not to vomit up the cup of chalk-like barium I had to drink. I wasn't sure if I could keep it down, and the nurse had kept insisting impatiently that I try harder. "If you throw up, you will have to drink it again, and you don't want that, now do you?"

I thought about what I really wanted: to be at my after school tennis practice instead of lying there half-naked in a flimsy gown, nauseous and trying to stay completely still on a sheet of cold metal, turning over at the command of a doctor.

I remember those first months of getting sick as being extremely overwhelming and confusing. I had never imagined that a person could feel so awful. I was constantly exhausted, nauseous, and an emotional wreck. No one seemed to understand how sick I felt, and as the tests kept coming back negative, most people thought it was an excuse on my part, that I was pretending to feel worse than I did to flake on my responsibilities. Everyone pressured me to push forward, to keep going with my normal routine: to do my homework, to smile, and to stop complaining. My parents wanted me to go to school and be a good student; my teachers wanted me to sit up straight and pay attention.

I started losing perception of who I was. I had been an active, social teenager with a black belt in karate who was about to be captain of the tennis team. A month later, I was so ill that when my friends and I went to the mall, we borrowed a wheelchair at the entrance so they could push me. I tried to make it feel fun and not as serious as it was, but inside I felt terrified.

Wake up, Amy. Wake up already from this nightmare.

Self-Reflection

- What did you feel when you first got your symptoms? Were you scared, angry, overwhelmed, confused?
- Did you first think that your symptoms would be temporary, or did you worry they would be chronic?
- When was the first time you contemplated that you might have an illness?
- Describe in detail a moment that has stood out for you, like this one in the doctor's office has for me.

5

WHAT IS ACCEPTANCE?

How do I embrace something that's ravaging my life?
How do I accept something I would do anything not to have?
How do I find peace with something that causes me incredible suffering?

Acceptance. The first thing that comes to mind is what acceptance isn't. It isn't resignation, apathy, or denial. It doesn't mean that I will stop taking steps to feel better or settle into a state of inaction. I can search within myself for acceptance while still searching outwardly for ways to feel better. After all, there are many factors to my physical and emotional health that I can change, such as my habits, my lifestyle, my diet, my self-care, my self-talk, and even my relationships.

I have spent the past sixteen years rethinking the way I live and actively taking care of myself. In many ways, I have indeed improved how I feel, but at the end of the day, I still have endometriosis, I still have inflammation, and I'm still limited in countless ways by my health. Acceptance doesn't mean I will give up trying to improve my circumstances. Acceptance means that I will stop being so *attached to the outcome* of my efforts to change. I can take action but without expectations. If the situation doesn't improve, I can accept that fact instead of becoming bitter or resentful. I can shift from hating my reality to being more neutral about it. Acceptance doesn't mean I won't get angry or sad at times—it means not living in those states.

Isn't that what acceptance is? Letting go of the pain, opening my heart to what is before me—even if it's ugly, even if it's not what I want. Acceptance doesn't mean that I like the situation or agree with it. It means understanding that the situation is what it is—it may not be where I want to be right now, but it's where I am nonetheless. Acceptance means being at peace with my circumstances *exactly as they are.*

I get that... but could I actually do it?

If I could be okay with things as they are, what would change for me? To start, acceptance would allow me to relate differently to my suffering, to my endometriosis, and to my body. I would live in a different world than the miserable one I live in now—one where anger and despair don't harden my heart. A world where I would forgive myself for having endometriosis and forgive my body for causing me so much pain. A world where I would still have joy, despite having a painful illness that devastates all aspects of my life. That world sounds beautiful and also so much better than the hateful one I'm lost in now.

May I find acceptance, and may it bring me peace.

Self-Reflection

- What do you think acceptance means?
- What do you think acceptance doesn't mean?
- What does acceptance of your illness mean to you?
- What benefits could acceptance bring to your life?
- List all the feelings you have about acceptance. For

example, anger, fear, discomfort, excitement, openness, jealousy. Do you have any hesitations toward acceptance or conflicting feelings?

- What is your strongest feeling when you think about accepting your illness?

6

LUCKY TO BE ALIVE

My friend and I left early this morning, driving eight hours to arrive at a remote national park in the southern United States. Now we sit here by our campfire, marveling at millions of stars winking at us from above. Far from any city, there is hardly any light pollution, so we are able to see the full expanse of the night sky. There is a certain magic in the stars, a mystery that sparks our imagination with questions of our existence while reminding us that we are just a tiny speck in the universe.

Tears come to my eyes. It has been so long since I have seen anything so breathtaking! The stars have awakened a feeling of awe inside of me that has been dead for ages. I feel incredibly lucky in this moment—lucky to be in a place witnessing such beauty, tranquility, and silence; lucky to contemplate the wonders of the grand world around me; lucky to be alive.

"Lucky to be alive." How funny it is to hear myself say these words. How many times have I cursed my existence? Frustrated, stressed, afraid, annoyed, pressured—these are all words that could sum up how I have felt for years now, since the onset of my symptoms. Certainly not happy. Definitely not "lucky to be alive." How could I feel that when my life has been filled with so much suffering?

Yet here I am, feeling grateful to be able to see the stars. I can understand now why people go to the lake, forest, or mountains to get away from the stress, the routine, the mundane, the busyness, the noise. Right now, under the sparkling sky, I even feel like I have gotten away from my illness.

Nature is revitalizing. The air here feels different; the warm night breeze makes me feel light and carefree. So I *am* capable of feeling joy! I've felt so empty inside, my sadness swallowing me up and blocking out all light, that I'd forgotten what joy was like.

I almost hadn't gone camping this weekend. It had seemed too hard. What would I eat? What if I got sick? Would my body be able to handle such a long car ride? But I had a longing to do something different than my usual weekend routine, so I promised myself that I would go even if it made me flare.

Now, I feel differently than I had before I left—like the heavy burden of my illness has been temporarily lifted off my shoulders. Will this feeling dissipate once I get back to the city and my routine? I think about how many times I've sat on my porch and looked up at the sky, never able to see more than a star or two. Yet the millions of stars above me are always there, even when I can't see them. This is what I need to remember throughout the dark times—the sacredness, the beauty, the awe of life is with us at all times. I may not always be able to see it, but perhaps I can learn to hold it in my heart.

Self-Reflection

- Recall a time when you felt a sense of awe, wonder, or amazement. It could be from a moment out in nature, a musical or art piece that you saw, a story you read or documentary you watched, an act of kindness that you witnessed or heard about.

- What happened?
- How did it make you feel? For example, did it bring warmth to your heart, help you feel more open and expansive, or leave you speechless?
- As you recall the memory, try to bring those same feelings into your body right now.

7

THE PATHWAY OF SELF-CRITICISM

About twelve years after I first got sick, I spent a year volunteering as a teacher in Achuar territory, in a small village of 150 people, deep in the Amazon rainforest. I didn't know if my body would be able to handle living in such a remote place, but I was relieved to find that the simpler living was right on par with the diet and lifestyle I had been following for years in an attempt to manage my symptoms. The fresh fish caught from the river and various fruit and vegetables grown from the local garden helped keep my inflammation and pain levels low. The complete lack of stress along with the fresh air did wonders for my mental health. Since there was no electricity, I went to bed soon after sundown, and woke up naturally at sunrise. Living in the Amazon, it was actually easier to follow my much-needed lifestyle because that was the only lifestyle available!

One day, I was invited to socialize at one of the villager's huts. I was supposed to take a path through the forest to get there, but once I had crossed the clearing, I found myself walking back and forth along the forest's edge, unable to find the path's opening. The forest was a dense mass of trees, ferns, and brush growing on top of each other, like a wall before me. After searching for several minutes, I finally found the path's narrow opening. It was about two feet wide, with just enough space for a person to pass.

This was the only path from the clearing to the villager's hut, so it was used every day by multiple people. Without their footsteps crushing the leaves and fallen branches underfoot, without their bodies clearing out the spiderwebs, and without their machetes hacking down the ever expanding tangle of branches, the path would be overrun with foliage and absorbed by the forest within just a few days.

I've recently been reading a lot about neuroscience and how the brain works. Our brains have neural pathways that our thoughts travel down, and each time we have the same thought, that neural pathway gets a little stronger and a little more likely to be taken again. Our thoughts take the familiar route by default. Just like the well-trodden forest path that was so much easier to traverse than hacking a new way through the thick forest brush, there are the same well-trodden neural pathways that our thoughts create in our brains. We reinforce these pathways each time we have similar thoughts. In my own case, I often berate myself or put myself down for all of my 'failures'. Every time I do that, I'm unknowingly fortifying the neural pathways of self-criticism, making it more likely that I'll have those thoughts again in the future. It's just like when villagers walk down the forest path—it clears out the overgrowth, making the path easier to walk down next time.

Because of these frequently used pathways, repeated thoughts often turn into thought patterns or habits without us realizing it. Until I began reading about the brain, I erroneously believed that the way I thought was set in stone: "This is who I am. I'm a person who angers easily. I'm a person who criticizes herself." But this isn't who I *have* to be, if I put enough work into it. Just like the villagers *could* create a new path through the forest, I *could* change my habits from always immediately criticizing myself to treating myself with patience and understanding. Even the most deeply entrenched thought patterns and conditioning can change; neuroscience has shown that this is possible at any age via neuroplasticity—the ability of the brain to change its neural connections and pathways. It takes effort to change a well-ingrained thought pattern, but it is 100% possible.

I didn't realize it at the time, but I've seen neuroplasticity in action when I was learning Spanish. On the first day I was in Spain studying abroad, I struggled to ask the waiter for a glass of water. I was terrible at Spanish and convinced that I would never be able to learn another language. But to my surprise, by the time I left a year later, I was able to speak about complex topics. With repetition and daily practice, the words kept coming out easier and faster, until one day they just came out automatically and I no longer had to struggle or search my brain for the vocabulary or grammar structure. By then, the neural pathways for speaking Spanish had become fortified in my brain.

However, once I left Spain and was no longer practicing daily, I started to lose that ability to speak so effortlessly. Thought patterns diminish when they are no longer being used, just like the narrow forest path would grow over if the villagers stopped walking along it.

At their core, my thoughts are a way of speaking to myself. If I want to 'forget' my pattern of critical self-talk, then I have to stop speaking that way. If I want to make being kind to myself my default, then I have to practice that language so those new neural pathways build in my brain.

Now that I have this understanding of how the brain works, I feel extremely motivated to have awareness of my thoughts. After all, it's only when I realize that an unwanted thought pattern has hijacked my mind that I can stop these thoughts in their tracks. As a start, I've been naming the thought pattern out loud as soon as I notice it, like: "Self-criticism." I try to do this without judging—I try to just 'witness' the thought as a casual observer. Otherwise it's easy to berate myself for criticizing myself, completely undermining this exercise and actually further reinforcing the unwanted thought pattern of negative self-talk!

I find myself saying the words "self-criticism" out loud many times a day. It shocks me how terribly I treat myself, especially when I have an endo flare. Interestingly, this is the time when I need the most self-compassion, but instead, I am filled with self-loathing, reflected in my vicious self-talk.

"Why did you eat that when you know that it makes you sick? You have no self-control."

"How could you not realize that you made those important plans during the week your period comes? Now, you have to cancel. You are so stupid to have made plans without checking your menstrual calendar first."

"You can't even walk up the stairs without getting tired?! You're pathetic."

"Well, you missed your friend's party, but it's probably better that way. Surely, they are tired of you and your illness."

"You are so weak. No one else falls on the floor sobbing and vomiting during their period."

As I pay attention to my thoughts and 'witness' them, I see that instead of accepting that my life can be hard, that I have an illness, and that it isn't my fault, I'm turning my back on myself. When I have a flare, I need gentleness, love, and understanding. But do I give that to myself? Never. Instead, I am harsh with myself, putting myself down in a way that I would never, ever speak to a loved one. I'm failing to recognize that these are awful, traumatic, painful situations that I am being thrown into. After all, I never had any training in how to cope with an illness that causes spontaneous debilitating flares that disrupt my life.

Our thought patterns are so powerful. It is worth examining

the way we speak about ourselves, our circumstances, and our illness. I truly believe that one of the most important keys to finding peace and happiness is in the way that we think. Depending on how we react to a situation, we can cut ourselves down or lift ourselves up. We can paralyze ourselves from taking life-changing action ("I'll never feel better... so why try") or push ourselves to do so ("Even though other doctors haven't known how to help, this new specialist is still worth a try—she might have the answers!"). We can convince ourselves that something is true or untrue ("My friends are probably tired of me") or we can objectively see the facts ("If my friends were tired of me, they wouldn't have invited me out. They understand that I have a disease I can't control").

I've been working on speaking a new language with myself, one that with time and repetition I will become fluent in, just as I did with Spanish. When I catch myself in a moment of self-hatred, I intentionally bring forward self-compassion. "You didn't do anything wrong," I tell myself out loud, cutting off the negative self-talk. "This happened because you have endometriosis. It's okay that this happened, and it isn't your fault. There's no reason to feel ashamed." Depending on the situation, I actively think of a time I felt successful, or smart, or whatever quality I'm denying in myself. This step helps me build new thought pathways in my brain to replace the old ones, reinforcing the idea that I am *not* these terrible names that I call myself.

If I would have tried to hack out a new forest path that day through the dense foliage of the jungle, it would have required a lot of effort and determination. It was naturally easier to just continue using the old path, the one that was well traveled and already there. This happens with the mind—our thoughts automatically run down the most used paths, reinforcing existing habits and patterns. But once we know that a path isn't good for us, wouldn't it be wiser to work on our thoughts to forge out a new way? It would take a lot of effort initially, but with repeated use, the new path would quickly end up as easy to use as the old one, except that this path would have an advantage—it would lead us to a better destination.

Self-Reflection

- What is your self-talk like?
- How do you treat yourself on a daily basis?
- What about when you feel you do something 'wrong'? Are you forgiving with yourself, or do you harshly judge yourself?
- What are some of the thought patterns that you have that are detrimental to you?
- How do you *want* to speak to yourself?
- Can you make an effort to catch yourself when you are self-critical and speak in a kinder way?

If you'd like to continue exploring changing your negative thought patterns, look into Cognitive Behavioral Therapy, which is a field of psychology filled with practical exercises to help retrain your brain.

8

CLIMBING OUT FROM ROCK BOTTOM

Note: This essay contains descriptions of pain that some readers may find upsetting.

Rock bottom. I find myself there emotionally right now. Any minute, without warning, my period is going to come. My partner can sense how distressed I am and keeps asking me if I'm okay.

I'm not okay. I try to find a way to describe my feelings so that they can be easily understood. "Imagine you are walking down an alleyway," I tell him, "and suddenly someone pops out of the shadow and starts bludgeoning you with a crowbar. Just as you're nearing death, you suddenly wake up, sweating, startled, breathing heavy. And you realize it was a dream! 'Ahhh!' you sigh in relief.

"But a few weeks later, you find yourself running errands in a new part of town. The street you're on feels oddly familiar, a little creepy, and you realize in terror that this is the street from your dream! Now you're on edge, full of dread, anxiety, and fear; you no longer feel safe or at ease.

"That's how I feel waiting for my period—like I'm walking

down a street where I already know what is going to happen and I'm just waiting in terror to be beaten to a pulp—perhaps while I'm at the supermarket, perhaps while in a meeting at work. After that happens, it takes all the strength, willpower, and energy left in me to tape myself back together again, climb out of the dark pit I find myself in, and try to heal both my body and my trauma."

My partner, who was listening quietly with a serious look on his face, hugs me tight. Although he is physically here with me, the loneliness I feel is overwhelming. Explanations still fall short of actually understanding the depth of the physical pain. Or how fear of that pain chokes my chest and makes it difficult to breathe the days before my period is going to come. Or how totally and completely broken I feel the days after, desperately trying to recover. Or how hopeless I feel: the worst days of my life are forever repeating themselves. My period is a chapter that never closes but is read and re-read every twenty-eight days. The book is so worn by now that the pages have crinkled and torn and fallen out. But don't worry, I know the words by heart.

Somehow, I always manage to get out from rock bottom. I've learned to keep a ladder down at the bottom of this dark hole, so that when I finally get my strength back, I can climb back up into the world where the sun shines, where people smile.

I can't smile right now. I sit here today, waiting for my period to come and wondering if I'm going to have to keep dragging myself up this ladder every month for the rest of my life.

Self-Reflection

- Are there flares that happen routinely that you know

are coming? For example, during your period, when you eat certain foods, or when you get stressed?

- How does it make you feel to know a flare is coming? Do you find it stressful, disheartening, frightening?
- How would you describe these feelings to someone who doesn't experience endometriosis flares?

9

OUR UNDENIABLE STRENGTH

Brutal.
What a fitting word for endometriosis pain.

Cruel.
Violent.
Torturous.
Excruciating.
Agonizing.
Soul-wrenching.
Intolerable.
Unbearable.
Unendurable.

Yet we *do* endure. We *do* survive the most crushing, torturous pain—both on a physical and emotional level. We watch endometriosis take away our fertility or our ability to work. We watch it devastate our relationships, our careers, and our hobbies. We experience symptoms that are unimaginable to most.

It's important to recognize how brutal the pain can be and not minimize it. In fact, I think it's vital that we don't sugarcoat our experiences. In the best of times, we face daily challenges. In the worst of times, we face unbearable pain. For me, recognizing how deeply I am suffering without trying to pretend everything is okay—especially on days when I feel anything *but* okay—has been one of the first steps in healing emotionally from the traumas of endometriosis. How can I accept endometriosis if I don't fully acknowledge the screaming pain, the grief of infertility, and the relentless exhaustion?

When we acknowledge how truly agonizing endometriosis can be, we are also recognizing our strength.

Our undeniable, incredible strength.

Yet most times, I don't feel strong at all. I ask myself, "What does strength look like?"

People can be terrified and still be strong.
Tears don't diminish a person's strength.
Strength can be present even if a person is overwhelmed.
Strength is putting one foot in front of the other.
It's a power we have inside all of us to keep going in the most soul-wrenching of times.

We are walking forward, doing the best we can. Our strength is growing, just like the mountains have been growing inch by inch each year since the beginning of time. Never forget that Mount Everest began as a flat plain, and now it rises majestically above the clouds.

Self-Reflection

- What does emotional strength mean to you?

- Do you think it grows with each challenge?
- What is an example of a time that you relied on your inner strength to get through a situation?
- Were you able to see your strength in that moment, or were you only able to recognize it in retrospect?

10

WHAT WOULD ENOUGH LOOK LIKE?

I have a few good days where my symptoms hardly bother me, but that's not enough—I want every day to be like that.

There are a few foods that don't make me sick, but that's not enough—I want to eat anything I choose, without restrictions.

I don't have everything that I want, and that hurts. Endometriosis is incurable, and that hurts. It's chronic, and that hurts. Many of my dreams were swallowed up by this disease, and that hurts.

At the same time, I'm stuck in a story about how nothing is ever enough. Not just in terms of my health—I also complain about not having enough time, money, or happiness. I'm chronically dissatisfied with all aspects of my life. From the seeds of want, suffering grows; the more I water these seeds, the faster and deeper my suffering grows.

It's okay to grieve for what I have lost. But if I have a deep-rooted attitude of always wanting more, then no matter how many symptom-free days I do have, it will never be enough. I love to blame endometriosis as the source of all my misery, but even if my endometriosis were magically cured, would it really change my inner dissatisfied attitude toward life? I might feel happy for a brief while, but once I got used to my new health, I would surely be on to wanting something else. I would quickly overlook the fact that I finally had what I've desperately wanted —my health—and focus on a new reason for disappointment and frustration in my life.

Even though I can logically see this, it's difficult to disentangle myself from my desires. I feel like a two-year-old having a tantrum, "But I want it! It's not fair! Give it to me!"

Can I open these clenched fists which I'm pounding on the floor in frustration? What I have is what I have. It's not about what I want. It's about what's right in front of me—a life with endometriosis. Can this life with this illness be enough for me?

For years, I've lived in protest: *I hate endometriosis! I can't live with this!* Yet where has this gotten me besides stuck in my anger? What if instead I got up and started to walk alongside my fate? It's inevitable, anyway. I can do it the easy way or the hard way. I can live with endometriosis, kicking and screaming, or I can live with endometriosis, thriving and loving my life anyway.

Which honestly seems unbelievable to suggest—*loving my life anyway.* But what if I do choose to consciously love my life anyway? What if I decide that my happiness will no longer be conditional on my wants and needs? What if I dare to shrug my shoulders and say, "I don't care!" to all the things that go wrong? What if I realize that while I don't have many pain-free days, the few I have are better than none at all?

I don't want to *pretend* that the circumstances don't upset me —I want to find myself in a place of peace where they *actually* don't upset me. I don't know if I will be able to get there, but I'm going to try. What I've been doing until now—letting anger and bitterness consume me—hasn't done anything but keep me locked in a state of misery. Time to stop fighting reality and do something different.

I'm going to make an attempt to move past my anger at my endometriosis and instead accept that my life is simply how my life is. I'm going to commit to opening my heart in gratitude to what I have: this breath that keeps me alive, some pain-free moments, and a willingness to practice letting go of what I want. That doesn't currently feel like enough, but as I continue down this path, hopefully one day it will be.

Self-Reflection

- Where do you see the concept of *it's never enough* in your own life?
- How much would be enough?
- Do you think that if you ended up getting all that you wanted, your idea of 'enough' would change and what you have would still fall short?
- Write out some ways in which you have 'enough.'
- Looking at all you have and in spite of what you don't have, do you think it's possible to *love your life anyway*? What do you think of this concept? Do you find it ridiculous, unattainable, a possibility for the future?

11

GET WELL SOON

A memory from college.

I was cleaning my room at my parent's house when I found a doll under my bed. It was a soft, stuffed troll with pink hair, wearing a green hospital gown that said, *Get well soon.* I had never seen this doll before, and when I asked my parents, they agreed it looked unfamiliar. It was a mystery as to how the doll ended up under my bed, but there it was. *Get well soon.*

The doll became my good luck charm, and I took her everywhere with me for years. She went to college with me, then abroad with me when I taught English both in Spain and Japan. I was really superstitious about her—after all, she had appeared out of nowhere with this message to me: *Get well soon*. She lived on my bed; whenever I entered my room and saw her looking uncomfortable, I adjusted her, fixed her hair, and told her I was sorry and that I loved her. I was so scared and lonely, but she gave me hope, comfort, and love.

I brought her to all of my doctors' appointments with me. In my second year of college when I went to see a new gynecologist, my *Get well soon* troll doll sat waiting for me in the car. The gynecologist listened to me talk about my symptoms, nodded, and said, "I think you may have endometriosis." She decided to do an exploratory laparoscopy, and a few weeks later, she made two small incisions and looked inside my abdominal cavity with a camera.

After the surgery, the gynecologist told me that she found nothing. In fact, according to her, I had the best looking ovaries and uterus she had ever seen.[1] I was nineteen years old at the time and had no idea that she wasn't an expert in endometriosis or that I even needed to seek out an expert. Looking back now, I believe she completely missed my endometriosis. Unfortunately, many gynecologists don't have adequate training to be able to recognize endometriosis in its various colors, forms, and locations throughout the body.[2]

The conclusion of that surgery was that I did not have endometriosis, and the doctor ruled it out as a possibility. It was supposed to be good news, but I felt disappointed. Every time another doctor found nothing wrong, I was no closer to getting better.

"You keep forming cysts on your ovaries that later rupture," the gynecologist told me. "Every month, the body makes a small cyst during ovulation to release the egg. In order to stop making cysts, I think we should stop your periods and your ovulation. I want to recommend a hormone shot that will do this for you."

She was looking at me, holding her prescription pad.

"I'm not sure," I finally said. "I mean, I haven't done well on five other types of birth control pills. They were supposed to help me manage my symptoms, but they made me incredibly sick, sicker than the symptoms themselves."

"I understand. But at the same time, this could be what you've been waiting for."

I really wanted her to be right. After three ruptured ovarian cysts in sixteen months—which seemed to be the cause of my pain and symptoms—someone was finally proposing a way to prevent them. It was hard to make a decision. I was exhausted. My whole body hurt, I hadn't eaten properly in weeks due to pain and diarrhea, and I was struggling just sitting there, never mind thinking about something important like this. I was also alone in the appointment and had no loved one there to talk it through with or give me advice. Nor had I learned yet the importance of doing self-research when it came to my medical care.

"Let's do it," I said, scared but hopeful.

"This is going to work." I whispered to myself over and over on the walk back to the car. "This will work." I had to believe it because I couldn't believe anything else. I couldn't be let down again. All I needed was hope.

I got in the car, my dolly in the passenger seat. *Get well soon.* "Okay, dolly," I said. "I will."

Self-Reflection

- Do you have anything that feels like a good luck charm to you, provides comfort, or has special meaning to you to help you get through the hard times? For example, a mantra or prayer that you say, a stuffed animal, a favorite heating pad, a crystal, a TV show that you always watch when you are sick.
- What is it about this that brings you comfort?
- What else do you do when you are in need of comfort?
- How do you soothe yourself when you feel sad, lonely, or upset?

12

FINDING MEANING IN THE MUNDANE

I've moved to Japan. I've always been fascinated with its language and culture, and I've found a job teaching English for a local Board of Education in a small city. I've been unable to work full-time for years, but this schedule is split shift, which has broken my day up into manageable chunks rather than a long, dragging eight hours. I teach a few hours in the morning and go home to eat lunch (which allows me to have my usual diarrhea in the privacy of my own bathroom!) Then, I can take a nap for an hour in the afternoon before teaching my evening classes.

In general, the lifestyle in Japan is fantastic for my endometriosis. To start, I walk everywhere. While this is hard on the days of severe pain, on most days the slow, daily movement is actually helping me to increase my endurance and keeps my aching body happier than when I'm not as active. Then there's the food. Staples of the Japanese diet, such as fresh fish, seaweed, and vegetables, are inherently anti-inflammatory. It's also much easier here than in the US to avoid foods that make me flare, since gluten, red meat, and dairy are not as common.

Even the snacks are drastically different, so there is a wider variety of food in Japan that doesn't make me sick.

What is helping me the most, however, is how I am learning to slow my life down and turn inwards. The Japanese are renowned for living long, healthy lives and have one of the highest life expectancies in the world. Apart from diet and lifestyle, it's been speculated that the Japanese live as long as they do because their lives are rich with meaning. Japanese culture has customs and traditions for eating, drinking tea, etiquette, and more. They have learned to turn tiny, mundane acts that most find insignificant—such as putting out fresh flowers or folding paper—into entire art forms. They have a strong appreciation of nature, from bamboo mats as floors in their homes to nationwide festivals to celebrate the change in seasons.

Life in this small town has a rich simplicity, and the more I experience the Japanese way of living, the more I learn that I can find meaning in anything. I had thought that for my life to have meaning I had to have some lofty purpose—children, a career that I felt passionately about, or some project that was changing the world. I don't have any of those, nor do I see myself having them anytime soon, but I'm finally learning that it's okay. Because actually, *I* assign meaning to the things in my life, and I can give meaning to whatever I choose.

Watching how my Japanese coworkers' and friends' eyes light up when they speak about their interests, I'm becoming aware that I don't have anything that gives me the kind of joy that I see on the faces of others around me. I don't have anything to give me a sense of purpose or a reason to wake up in the morning. There is a serious lack of meaning in my life. Is that what this hole is that I feel in my heart? All this time, I thought it had been carved out by the severe physical pain, but I realize now that even if I woke up one day and my dream of no longer having endometriosis came true, my life would still feel empty.

A few years before I moved to Japan, my friends and I went to the movie theatre to see *Alice in Wonderland* in 3D. During the 108 minutes, I had to urgently take several trips to the bathroom, and I missed a good chunk of the movie. Still, from what I saw, I loved the storyline. It took me to a faraway land, a fantastical place where people didn't almost poop themselves daily. Alice was on an exciting adventure, not incapacitated in bed for hours from pain.

When the movie ended and it was time to get up from our seats, I literally couldn't. A deep feeling of emptiness drained all my energy from me. The mesmerizing journey that I had escaped into for the past two hours was over. Now I was back to my awful life of pain, incontinence, and nausea.

I started sobbing and couldn't stop, no matter how hard I tried to pull myself together. My friends stared at me through their 3D glasses, asking me what was wrong, asking if I was okay. I wasn't okay. I didn't know if I was ever going to be okay. All I knew was that now that *Alice in Wonderland* was over, it was back to real life for me—a life I didn't want to be in. I wanted to be alive, but I didn't want to be in *my* life.

"What is the point of it all?" I asked them, tears streaming down my face. "To get up, day after day, only to have a life full of pain and suffering? Life is miserable. What are we living for?" They didn't know how to answer, and neither did I.

For years, I felt lost, overpowered by a sadness deep in my soul. But in this small town in the Japanese countryside, with its ceremonies for drinking tea and all-day picnics for viewing the cherry blossoms, I'm starting to find my way. It's clear to me now that we create our own *personal* meaning in life. *We* decide what we live for. The reason may change throughout our lives, as we go through different stages and seasons. The reasons will be different for each of us, but we all need ways to feel more alive.

Witnessing how the people here find joy so easily, it's

dawned on me that all of this time, I have been looking for meaning in the wrong place. Fulfilment doesn't just come from special experiences, like falling in love or taking a trip. Fulfilment can also come from a library book, a favorite TV show, a facemask, organizing the closet, looking out the window at the clouds in the sky, and even the moments where nothing is happening except that my nausea has finally subsided.

A wise teaching from the Buddha is that life has 10,000 joys *and* 10,000 sorrows. This world is full of both magnificence *and* misery. So how can I bring in more presence to stop overlooking the seemingly insignificant and instead use it to experience my 10,000 joys? How can I make intentional spaces in my life to slow down and appreciate what's before me?

I'm beginning to cultivate purpose in my life. It's nothing big or fancy, but now I know it doesn't need to be. Eating a few squares of chocolate, listening to music, curling up in a comfortable blanket to watch a movie—these activities break up the monotony of being sick and balance out the pain. I don't have to know 'the point of it all'. I only have to know the point of *right now*.

Self-Reflection

- Do you think that we each create our own personal meaning in life?
- Do you think reasons for meaning change throughout our lives?
- Is it possible to find meaning in seemingly insignificant experiences, like drinking a cup of tea or listening to music?
- What gives you a sense of fulfilment and meaning?
- Does having meaning or not having meaning change your relationship with your life?

13

WEAVING THE STRANDS OF ACCEPTANCE

I'm walking the nature trail behind my workplace, passing spiderweb after spiderweb. I stop to examine one, impressed with how delicate yet sturdy it is. It's a dense web about four feet in diameter, with a small spider resting gracefully in the center of its creation. Yesterday morning when I walked this path, this particular spiderweb wasn't here. How quickly the spider was able to weave this web from nothing! And if something were to bring it down, the spider would just rebuild. It wouldn't cry about the loss. It would just diligently get to work making a new web, one strand at a time, persevering until it was finished.

Whenever I am out in nature, it always provides me insight. Today, I am reminded of two things: that goals are reached one step at a time, and that everything begins within.

One step at a time—that's how I am changing the way I feel about my endometriosis and my life. Through learning different practices like self-awareness, changing my thought patterns, and cultivating patience, I am weaving my web of acceptance. It will take longer than a few days to build this web of mine, but it isn't an impossible goal. Slowly and steadily, I can find the same peace and tranquility I see in this spider hanging here before me.

These qualities already live inside of me, along with many others, just as the silk that made this web came from inside of the spider. Everything that I need is already within me. People talk about 'tapping into' their inner resources or 'uncovering' their true nature—I just need to learn how to access my own. I remember as a child how fascinated I was the first time my father tapped the maple trees in our yard to make maple syrup. He made a hole in each tree a few inches in diameter, inserted a spout with a hanging bucket, and, over the course of a month, the sweet clear sap flowed out and filled the bucket, which we would then boil down into maple syrup. One step at a time, with a bit of work, the sap hidden within the tree turned into something wonderful. Until you tap into the tree, you would have no idea that such sweetness is flowing inside of it.

Although I live in a city and often feel far removed from the natural world, I, too, am a part of nature. Just like the maple tree with its syrup, just like the spider with its silk, I also have resources inside of me—universal human qualities, such as strength, perseverance, and resilience. I just have to know they are within and keep learning ways to access them.

Self-Reflection

- What are the 'strands' that are weaving your web of acceptance (for example, self-awareness, examining thought patterns, cultivating patience)?
- What human qualities do you want to tap into inside of yourself?
- What practices do you do that are uncovering them?
- Are there any new practices you haven't done yet but want to try? What's stopping you from doing them?

14

THE STORIES I TELL MYSELF

During the year I spent with the Achuar on their land, I would frequently stargaze at the community clearing. Since the village was located deep in the Amazon rainforest, with no light pollution for thousands of miles, I could see the beauty of millions of stars in the stunning sky above.

It was only a ten minute walk to the clearing. I took this narrow path multiple times every day to go from my cabin to the field to watch the students play soccer or to visit the huts of families in that area. Whenever it rained, the dirt would turn to mud, and once the rain ended, butterflies would gather in the mud puddles to take in salts and minerals. On those days, in my attempt to take pictures of the bright green patterns on their wings, I would slowly inch my way down the path toward these magnificent creatures. In my effort not to scare away the butterflies as I approached, I would walk with my body pressed against the jungle that flanked the path, so close at times that my clothes would pick up spiderwebs.

There were no butterflies out in the evenings, but the stars awaited me. Excited, I set off on the path as I had countless times before. The village was silent, but this was normal, as many were probably already asleep. Since the sun went down a few hours ago and there was no electricity in the village, it was almost pitch black. The moon tonight was just a tiny sliver in the sky and hardly provided any light.

I'd only gone a third of the way when I heard a loud rustling in the bushes. My first thought was that it was just the wind. Still, I moved to walk down the middle of the six-feet-wide path, distancing myself as much as I could from the jungle on my sides. The noise in the bushes got closer, like it was approaching me. "There's nothing there," I reassured myself. "Don't be silly."

I looked in that direction, shining my flashlight over the shrubs and leaves. The dense layers of ferns, foliage, and vines cast eerie shadows as my light passed over them. That, coupled with the darkness of the night, felt like the perfect setting for some unknown force to reach out from between the trees and grab my leg. My heart began thudding loudly in my chest and I quickened my step. "You've watched too many scary movies. Who is going to grab you?" I asked myself logically, trying to stay calm. "You walk this path all the time. You know there is nothing here."

I was so busy shining my light anxiously over the trees on my right side that I didn't illuminate the path in front of me as I walked. I tripped over a root, falling to my knees, my flashlight flying out of my hand. At that exact moment, the wind picked up and howled. I fumbled clumsily for my flashlight, fear washing over me. As the wind rustled the trees, they shook spookily in the ominous darkness and gave me the impression that the already narrow path was closing in on me—the jungle and whatever mysterious creatures that abided in it was about to swallow me up! I hurried to my feet in a full panic, running terrified and as fast as I could to the clearing.

I burst out of the path and into the wide open field, rushing to the middle of it. Out of breath, dirt on my knees from the fall,

I spun around wildly, frantically aiming my flashlight in every direction, sure that some spirit or creature or sinister force was about to come up from behind and pull me into its darkness.

After a few minutes had gone by and nothing had attacked me, I managed to calm down and the terror faded. I finally felt confident enough to turn off my flashlight to stare up at the sky above, which was no longer obstructed by the trees. I was not disappointed. Millions of stars danced in the beauty of the night, their glittering light putting everything into perspective. As the last of the adrenaline disappeared from my body, so did the fear from my mind. I burst out laughing at how ridiculous that whole situation had been.

I lay down in the field for a while, enjoying the twinkling of the impressive, glorious stars, then headed back on the path to my cabin—calmly this time, the way I usually walked the path. I chuckled at the terror that overtook me just thirty minutes earlier. "You are so ridiculous," I told myself, shaking my head.

As I replayed the situation in my mind, it became clear to me that the demons weren't in the forest before me—they were in my mind! Oh, how the mind loves making things up, getting lost in its fears, imagining the worst. It's really no different than the fear-based thoughts that frequently invade my mind about my illness. I am as carried away by these untrue thoughts as I was by the sounds of the evening wind. Thoughts like:

I will never feel better.
I am a burden.
No one will love me because I have a chronic illness.
My body is broken.
This is my fault.
I don't deserve to feel better.
Now that I'm sick, I will never be happy again.
Endometriosis is ruining my life.

Beliefs like these box me into limiting ideas about my health and life. They diminish my capability to be happy and negatively influence my decisions and actions. Ideas like 'I will never feel better' and 'I don't deserve to feel better' cause me to give up before I ever try—why bother, if I will never feel better anyway? Why start a relationship, if 'no one will ever love me because of my illness'?

Through meditation, I have been observing my thoughts, and I've realized that I am excellent at inventing stories around facts. It's a fact that I have endometriosis, but the rest are not facts! For example, take my belief that I will never feel better. How did I jump to that pessimistic conclusion? While endometriosis is incurable, symptoms can be managed with diet, lifestyle, hormones, and many other ways—ways that I already have been actively using for years to help improve my symptoms! But in spite of factual evidence to the contrary, I cling to this idea that I am doomed to feel terrible my whole life.

What a relief it is to realize that not everything my mind says is true. The more I meditate and watch my thoughts go through my mind, the clearer it is that my mind spews lies like a volcano overflowing with lava. The mind loves tormenting me with needless worries, and its incessant criticism is poisoning me, inventing reasons constantly as to why there is something wrong with me: My body is broken, I am unlovable, I'll never be enough, my illness is my fault, I am failing at healing, I am a burden to others. It's all lies! I'll never be happy if I live my life believing them, and yet that's exactly what I've been doing.

As I cultivate awareness—as I meditate daily and actively pay attention to what I'm thinking about—it's allowing me to be a 'witness' to the thoughts and stories of my mind and see them as exactly that: thoughts and stories. I've been finding it helpful to name out loud what my mind is doing in those moments: "Judging." "Worrying." "Blaming." "Jumping to conclusions." When I can identify what the thought is, I can get distance and separation from it, and that makes it easier to untangle myself from it and realize that it's not true. For example, when I catch myself jumping to the conclusion that I am unlovable, I can tell myself, "There are millions of people with endometriosis that have healthy, happy relationships. I'm judging myself and jumping to conclusions. Just because it hasn't happened to me yet doesn't mean it never will."

I've been trapped in negativity and fear, but I'm waking up to the way the mind works. I'm excited to understand the habits of my own mind and invite in new beliefs that won't limit my health and life. I *do* deserve to feel better, and I won't let my mind cause me to give up before I ever try.

Self-Reflection

What are some stories that you tell yourself about your illness? For example:

I will never feel better.
I am a burden.
No one will love me because I have a chronic illness.
My body is broken.
This is my fault.
I don't deserve to feel better.
I will never be happy again.

- Do you perceive any of these beliefs as true for you? Write down all of the negative beliefs (including your own) that you have about your illness and yourself as someone with an illness.
- If you take a few minutes to think about them, do you think that any of your beliefs may actually *not* be true?
- Take one of your beliefs and explore it further. Why do you think you have this belief?

- Can you think of evidence against this belief? What new conclusions can you come to? For example, if you look at *'my body is broken,'* you might think this is true because you are constantly in pain, fatigued, and with digestive problems. Yet evidence to the contrary might be that your body is still able to walk, pick items up, see, hear, and breathe, all on its own. Your new conclusion might be, *my body isn't broken, but, rather, it has some health problems.*

15

UNTANGLING MYSELF FROM MY THOUGHTS

Have you ever stopped to think about what exactly thoughts are? Our minds are often filled with a constant barrage of them: judgments, plans, worries, criticisms, regrets, nostalgias, resentments. Thoughts can transport us to the past or the future; they can take us on wild, uncomfortable, and even terrifying rides of unnecessary and unhelpful rumination, downward spirals, and highly unlikely 'what if' catastrophes.

How often am I swept away by my thoughts while completely oblivious to the moment right in front of me, a moment that might hold great beauty and happiness? How often am I convinced by my thoughts that I have less value than I do: that I am incapable, ugly, or worthless? How often do I have anxiety because of my fearful thoughts of the future when in reality, in this actual moment, I'm okay?

Thoughts are ideas and opinions that arise in the mind, often passing through very quickly, dissolving right into the next thought. They are extremely powerful, but I didn't understand this until I started watching them through meditation. Our thoughts shape our reality, influencing our mood, emotions, efforts, actions, reactions, decisions, behavior, and how we engage with the world. All of those aspects, in turn, influence our thoughts in a perpetual cycle.

Many of our thoughts are patterns, stories, or beliefs that have been programmed into our subconscious mind, often before we are even seven years old![1] My thoughts were conditioned into me as I soaked up what I saw and heard around me: the behaviors and words of parents, caretakers, teachers, people on TV, peers, bullies, and even strangers we passed in the grocery store. My thoughts are an amalgamation of the opinions, ideas, and judgments I have absorbed throughout my lifetime; they are influenced by my education, culture, and people around me. My thoughts were learned—they are not ultimate truths. And now? One of the greatest gifts meditation has brought me is that I no longer believe every judgment, thought, and criticism that crosses my mind, especially the ones about myself.

Becoming aware of my thoughts is freeing. To notice that I am creating a fictional story around the facts—a story that feels so true even though it isn't! To notice how I blame, worry needlessly, and close off to the world. To notice that I've been swept away by thoughts and then disengage with them to come back to the present moment. To notice that there *is* space between my thoughts (which seem to all run into each other one after another) and cultivate that space to have more inner calm.

I remember once when I went scuba diving. After I jumped off the boat and into the ocean, the small choppy waves threw me about, and I found myself quickly getting nauseous. But as soon as I got underneath the surface by a few feet, the water below was calm. I found myself inside of a vastness and serenity that I hadn't known existed, and I was blown away by the peace and beauty within the ocean. Meditating reminds me of this experience. With practice, we can dive under the relentless, frenzied chatter of our mind to discover our awareness and the stillness and peace that exists within ourselves.

Self-Reflection

Have you ever tried meditating? There are many types of meditation, such as Vipassana, guided meditations, Qigong, and chanting. There are apps, online videos, downloadable audios, in-person retreats, and more, all with different teachers. If you are interested in meditating, I encourage you to try out different styles and teachers to see which ones you prefer. You may hate sitting quietly but love Qigong (slow standing movements combined with breathing), or you may find it hard to meditate from online videos and instead prefer to go to a local meditation meetup each weekend!

Today, let's meditate for five minutes. It's okay if you've never meditated before; we'll do it together.

First, find a comfortable position sitting or lying down (though it's what you may frequently see in art, you do not have to sit cross legged unless you'd like to).

When you are ready, set a timer for five minutes and close your eyes. Focus on your breath flowing in and out. Don't change your breathing to be faster or slower, just notice it. Notice its speed, how it moves your chest or stomach, how it feels in your body. If it helps you to concentrate on your breath, you can think *inhale, exhale* while you breathe in and out, or count your breaths—just up to ten, and then start again at one.

While you're breathing, thoughts will come to your mind. That's totally expected and normal. Try to watch your thoughts without actively engaging in them. For example, if a thought comes in about how you should clean the kitchen later, don't start thinking about what needs cleaning, how long it will take, or how the bathroom also needs cleaning. If you do go down the rabbit hole of a thought, that's okay. You are not doing anything wrong—there's no need to judge yourself or feel that you are awful at meditating. All you need to do is go back to focusing on your breath. When you catch your mind engaging in a thought, it can be helpful to label the thought for what it is. For example, you can say, "planning / worrying / obsessing / judging / wanting / hating." Then, go right back to focusing on your breath.

It will be challenging at first not to get swept away by your thoughts, so don't worry about how often it happens. Just keep going back to the breath when you notice that your mind has wandered. If you practice this daily, even for only five minutes, you will find yourself able to disengage from wandering thoughts and return to the present moment a little faster each time.

16

NO MORE OPTIONS

A memory from college.

Morning sickness. Hot flashes. Mood swings. Fatigue. Full body pain.

Although three months had gone by since I had taken a hormone shot that was supposed to help relieve me of my symptoms, the side effects remained intolerable. I actually hadn't had diarrhea during that time, but to be honest, it would have been preferable to the five hours of relentless nausea each morning. I was miserable and decided to have an ultrasound with my gynecologist.

The results came back—a cyst. Exactly what this medication was supposed to prevent. Tears of frustration and defeat came to my eyes as the gynecologist pointed out my cyst on the ultrasound.

"What should we do?" I asked.

"I think you should take the next dose of the shot," the gynecologist said.

"How can you say that?" I felt confused and, honestly, a little betrayed. "It's supposed to prevent me from having more cysts, and yet, I have a cyst."

"But look at the whole picture," she insisted. "You don't have diarrhea. Isn't that good?"

"That's true," I said. "But I feel worse. The side effects of this shot have been a nightmare. I'm not going to take it again."

The gynecologist looked at me with an expression of frustration on her face. After a long pause, she said, "Well, I don't know what else to prescribe. You've now tried six types of birth control in two years, and none of them have helped. There are just no more options.[1] You will simply need to learn how to live with this."

I nodded. "Okay."

Don't cry, Amy. I didn't cry. I think I was numb. But as soon as I got into my car and saw my dolly waiting loyally for me in the passenger seat, I started weeping uncontrollably. "I was so excited," I choked out, talking to her. "The doctor is nice, but she said she can't help me. I don't know what else to do."

Get well soon, my dolly's green nurse's outfit lied. I clutched her to my chest.

"I'm scared," I said in between sobs. "I don't know if I will ever get better."

Self-Reflection

Think about a time when you felt disappointed by the medical system. For example, when you had hoped a medicine would work that didn't, when you thought a doctor would listen or provide a solution but didn't, when a surgery didn't have the outcome you had hoped for. What did you hope would happen?

- What actually happened?
- What did you feel at the time?
- What do you feel looking back on it now?

17

IMPERMANENCE

The inescapable truth is that nothing lasts forever. Not our bodies, not the day, not the apple on my counter that turned brown only an hour after cutting it in half.

I clearly remember the first day I experienced endometriosis symptoms. It was a Wednesday afternoon: January 2nd, 2002. I wasn't hungry for the ham sandwich I usually ate for lunch, which was strange because that was my favorite food at the time. That day however, the fluffy potato bread, spicy mustard, cheese, and tomato slices didn't look appealing at all. I hesitantly took a bite anyway but felt nauseous and had to spit it out. That was the moment my life began to unravel.

It's incredible what the mind remembers, even years later. It's been over a decade, but I can still remember sitting in the school cafeteria with my friends, remarking to them how odd it was that I had no appetite for my lunch. I can clearly pinpoint that lunch as the moment I started feeling sick; in fact, a few hours later, the throbbing cramps and nonstop diarrhea arrived. Little did I know at the time, but the cramps and diarrhea would stay by my side for the next two years.

That was the day after the New Year. It was the first day of my final semester of high school, and I was filled with dreams and excitement about my future, especially about going off to college. I never imagined that I would begin suffering from endometriosis. On that afternoon—an afternoon like any other —my life started to turn upside down. Within a few days, it felt like I had been catapulted into a life that I didn't recognize. It blew me away. It wasn't just the severity of the symptoms I suddenly had to deal with; it was the shock of my world breaking around me. I was not prepared for the life lesson that everything is impermanent: the healthy teenager that I was until that day was actually an impermanent state of being. That joyful girl was gone; in her place, there was another confused, overwhelmed girl now suffering from endometriosis symptoms. How deeply I grieved that loss of identity in the many years that followed.

The other day, I looked at pictures of myself in high school. I no longer look anything like the scared seventeen-year-old girl that was having frequent and urgent diarrhea. Nor do I look like the twenty-five-year-old woman who thought in a moment of desperation about ending her life. When I look in the mirror, my thirty-three-year-old self stares back at me. "Hello," I tell her. She won't be here forever, either. In another five to ten years, I'll be seeing an older version of myself with more wrinkles and gray hairs. At some point, I will be in a coffin in the ground, a skeleton without my recognizable features.

How morbid, I think to myself. And yet, it's the truth, as well as a reminder that life has given me a fleeting, impermanent chance: to be here, to see the sunrises and sunsets, for things to go well at times and awful during others, to love and also have my heart broken, to feel on top of the world some days and in absolute darkness in others. All of those experiences are connected by change.

Change is what brings about life; change is what ends life. Change is inescapable. If I could embrace it and stop wishing with every bone in my body that life would just go back to 'the way it was,' then I could live in peace instead of in disappointment and sadness. Perhaps a huge step to accepting endometriosis is accepting the undeniable reality that circumstances are constantly changing.

If I were to really understand that everything is fleeting, would I feel less shocked by change? Would I be better able to cope when circumstances change for the worse? Would I feel less upset if I truly understood that life is unpredictable, can go in a million ways for us, and that there is no one 'right way' for it to go? Would I cherish what I had before me even more, knowing that one day, it would be gone?

Now that my eyes are open to impermanence, I see it everywhere. I glance over at the candle that is lit on my desk. It's nighttime and the room is dark apart from the candle's soft glow. I watch it calmly, focusing on the flicker of the flame. The flame is not the same one it was a few seconds ago. The light and warm glow it gives off is the same, yet the flame itself dances and jumps on the wick. With each flicker, the flame has changed.

The wax below the flame has softened and is melting; small drops periodically roll down the long candlestick and dry toward the bottom. In several hours, the candle will melt down completely, its lifespan limited by its wax just as mine is limited by the natural laws of physics.

It is all impermanent, and whether that is positive or negative depends on the meaning I assign to it. This candle burns without regard for pain, a ham sandwich, or grey hairs. Its flame glows steady throughout its lifetime until finally the flame is extinguished. The flame reminds me of my soul, giving off continuous light in its life, yet changing constantly.

Can I face changing circumstances with the same steadiness as this flame? Can I take advantage of my lifetime and live it fully before my own candle burns out? Can I continue to shine brightly no matter what life brings?

Self-Reflection

- What comes to mind when you hear the word 'impermanence'?
- What are your general feelings toward change and why? Do you embrace it? Does it make you nervous or afraid?
- Can you think of a time that change has made you suffer?
- What about a time when it has made you relieved or happy?
- What attitude would you like to have toward change?
- Is that different from the attitude you have now toward it?

18

GRATITUDE AMIDST SUFFERING

I told myself that I would start to pay attention to all that I have been taking for granted, but unfortunately, I continue to be lost in my thoughts of wanting more—more foods that don't make me sick, more nights without insomnia, and especially more pain-free days. This weekend, however, I was reminded of my commitment to be grateful for what I have. I saw a powerful movie called *Run Boy Run* about an eight-year-old boy who fled the Warsaw ghetto to escape Nazi persecution. He spent three years slipping between villages and trying to survive in the forest; it is based on a true story.

It never ceases to amaze me how people have survived the most unimaginable situations. The will, the determination, and the unbelievable mental strength that humans across the world have inspires me.

This movie has awakened in me a deep gratitude. There are so many simple but important truths I take completely for granted: I am not being hunted; I'm not at war; I'm not on the run. If someone were chasing me during a debilitating pain flare, I wouldn't have any chance of surviving. Instead, I'm safe and able to keel over in pain in the familiarity of my home. How difficult would it be to not have a home to be in at all—especially during my period? To have no toilet, comfort, or privacy? To be completely alone, without family or friends?

Guilt rises up in me. Here I am whining about how I want to have a pain-free bowel movement when I still have a far better overall situation than so many others in the world. I feel disgusted with myself: I have been so completely oblivious to the good in my life that it has taken a movie about the unspeakable horrors of the Holocaust inflicted on a child to wake me up from my internal monologue of "Why me?!" I am furious with myself for how deeply I am trapped in a victim mindset; thoughts of "My life is so hard and it's not fair! Why is this happening to me of all people?" keep pulling me back in, no matter how many times I've tried to break them.

"What is wrong with you?!" I ask myself out loud. My face burns with shame remembering a scene of the boy hiding from the Nazis. Sure, my life with this illness has felt hard, but my hardships have been nothing like what he and so many survive. "Why can't you understand how good you have it?" I berate myself.

But wait—haven't I been establishing that the way I think has been learned and is mostly a habit and a pattern? That the more I think a certain way, the more I'm likely to continue thinking that way unless I consciously try to change? In fact, at this exact moment, I'm unwantedly doing one of my common habits: self-criticism. And how does being constantly self-critical help me? It doesn't. It won't bring perspective, it won't bring gratitude, it won't bring peace. All self-criticism does is make me feel bad—and do I really want to berate myself my entire life?

I take a few breaths, trying to bring in kindness. I need to be gentle with myself. Yes, I have been very ignorant of the good in my life, but I don't need to hate myself for that. What I can do instead, which is much more helpful than guilt and self-loathing, is make a commitment to cultivate gratitude and notice the good in my life.

In my own life, yes, many things are going wrong for me but a lot is still going *right*. I've seen so much of my life in a binary sense: a situation is either good or bad, happy or sad. What if I could acknowledge *both* sides, instead of ignoring one or the other? I don't need to see the world from the viewpoint that I am a victim and that only awful things happen to me; at the same time, I don't need to downplay the difficulties and gloss them over with toxic positivity. I can acknowledge that circumstances in some areas of my life are miserable and not ideal, while in others, I am privileged. For example, it's heartbreaking that I have a chronic illness, but it's wonderful that I'm good at researching, which helps me find solutions to many of my health problems. It's horrible that most doctors haven't known how to help me, but it's a privilege to be born in a place with access to advanced medical care, allowing me to see several types of specialists and get all kinds of tests done. It's depressing and challenging to have so many food intolerances, but it's a huge help that I can order online for a variety of food and supplements and get them delivered right to my door.

Life is much more nuanced than I previously noticed. There has been so much good—but I haven't seen it; I've been too busy pining over what I *don't* have to notice what I *do* have. It's like when the sun went down when I was living in the rainforest. There was no electricity, so at night the bright world turned black. When I turned on my flashlight, whatever the beam was shining on was the only thing I saw, surrounded by shadows and indistinguishable darkness. Out of focus from my light, it felt like nothing else existed.

Can I stop focusing my emotional flashlight on only the bad in my life and, instead, expand it to include the good? Can I hold space in my heart for both? Ever since I got sick, I've been collecting reasons why my life is horrible, reasons why everything is going wrong. Is that the path to happiness? No. But being able to see the bigger picture and appreciate aspects of my life that are going well can indeed lead to greater satisfaction with life, more joy, and more contentment. If I can see the things that are going right in my life, I think I have a chance at figuring out how to be okay even though things are also going wrong.

Starting right now, I'm making a commitment to have more gratitude. Every day, I will find at least three reasons:

Today, I am grateful to have witnessed and been inspired by the strength of this eight-year-old boy.
Today, I am grateful that I am starting to cultivate gratitude, which will help me find more joy in my life.
Today, I am grateful for the clay bowl on my shelf, which was a gift from my students in the Amazon, because it reminds me of the beautiful year I spent in their village and moments we shared.

I close my eyes for a minute and take a deep breath. As I breathe in, the warmth and openness of gratitude fills my heart. It's a feeling that has been mostly foreign to me, but I welcome it and vow to make appreciation and happiness as normal in my life as the feeling of pain.

Self-Reflection

What are three things that you feel grateful for today? Take a minute to think before completing the sentences below. Don't write something that you think you should be grateful for but something that you actually feel grateful for—remember, no one sees this but you! It can be anything, big or small.

Today, I am grateful...
Today, I am grateful...

Today, I am grateful...

After you write your sentences, expand on them. Why are you grateful for these things? Now, sit for a minute and really feel your gratitude in your body. What does it feel like?

If you were to write down every day three reasons why you are grateful, do you think you would feel any differently toward your life at the end of a week? A month? Six months? Do you want to try this exercise?

19

WORKING TOGETHER WITH MY BODY

Mount Fuji. It's a gorgeously symmetrical mountain with a snow-capped cone, rising up 12,388 feet (3,776 meters).

Recently, I went with a large group of twenty friends to climb it. We rented a small bus, parked at the base, and started the trail at night so that we would be on the top of the mountain by sunrise. It's not supposed to be a difficult climb (one walks up a well-defined trail), but it certainly was for a body like mine wracked with pain and fatigue.

I couldn't keep up with the group at all. I ended up hours behind them, trudging steadily forward, determined to make it as far as I could, with a close friend who said she didn't mind my slow pace. We didn't make it to the top by the time the sun rose, which was our goal, but we did make it above the clouds by dawn. The pink hues on the horizon and ability to see for miles in every direction was breathtaking. The golden sunlight streamed on the rocks around us, bathing us in warmth as we continued slowly to the top. When we finally made it, tears came to my eyes, and my friend looked over at me. She nodded in understanding. "Yeah," she commented. "It's pretty amazing to fight against your body and push yourself to the top."

I shook my head. I hadn't fought against my body. For the first time in a long while, I had cooperated with my body, and my body with me, to find myself before this incredible view. Although my body was literally shaking from the exertion, it hadn't felt like a fight at all. On the way up, when my body felt tired, I slowed down—but I kept going. When my body felt like it couldn't go any further, I sat down on the side of the path and rested—but then I stood up and kept going.

It's common to use militaristic language when we talk about being sick. We combat, destroy, beat, battle, and conquer our illnesses. We tell ourselves to keep fighting and call ourselves warriors. That mindset is one I held for over a decade; it helps many people and there is nothing wrong with it. But I realized that it's not the right mindset for *me* as an individual. I had thought that if I wasn't fighting, it meant I was giving up, or that I was letting illness win. But now I'm realizing that if I'm fighting against endometriosis, then it is indeed winning. For me personally, I can't be at peace or be happy if I'm constantly at war with a part of myself. That day walking up Mount Fuji, I realized that I don't want to fight anymore. Instead, I want to surrender to the reality that I have a disease, and work together with my body to climb all of the metaphorical mountains endometriosis puts before me.

For me, fighting means I am resisting: although I follow lifestyle practices to help me manage flares, for years I've hated and resisted against these practices. Why? Because in actuality, I want my body to be different than it is. I don't want to have special routines every day just to feel somewhat less uncomfortable in my own body—so every day, it's a fight to eat my anti-inflammatory diet, a fight to go to bed early, a fight to manage my stress. All that fighting is so incredibly exhausting—and I'm already tired enough from my endometriosis symptoms as it is!

But working *together* with endometriosis means seeing these practices not as fights but as acts of self-love and self-care to myself, a person who has a disease. It's making changes to cooperate with endometriosis and striving to have the best possible outcome for my body—not striving to beat endometriosis. This disease is chronic and has no cure. It's a part of my life, a part of my body, a part of my journey. I don't want to battle a part of my life. I want to welcome all of my life, and say, "This is how it is—and that's okay."

That is exactly what I did with this climb up Mount Fuji. I acknowledged the fact that I didn't know if I would be able to climb a mountain as a person with fatigue and pain. I told myself that if I tried but ended up having to turn around (or worse, be carried back down to the base due to a flare), that it would be okay. It wouldn't mean that I was a failure or inadequate. I also recognized that I would need to work together with my endometriosis, so I took the day before the climb off work and relaxed in bed, napping as much as possible to gather energy. I took two days off after the climb as well, so I wouldn't have to push myself to get back to work after such physical exertion. I bought a walking stick to lean on. I packed only the essential to keep my bag light: stick-on heating pads, painkillers, electrolytes, and snacks that would give me energy but not flares.

My body and I made it to the top together because I listened to what my body needed. It's true that I made it up the mountain six hours slower than my group of friends. They poked fun at me when I finally arrived at the hotel we were staying at. "You took forever!" they said. But I just laughed, overjoyed that I had made it at all. It didn't matter if the time I took was longer than anyone else—in the end, we had both scaled the 12,388 feet to the top! This has shown me that I shouldn't underestimate myself just because of my endometriosis. With extra time and extra accommodation, I, too, can achieve my dreams and goals.

Of course, patience and timing is important too. Several years ago, ascending a mountain would have been impossible. At that time, going up a flight of stairs was too much of a challenge. But my circumstances have improved, and with that, what I am capable of.

My experience on Fuji is symbolic to me of the progress I've made with my health and the heights I can get to if I'm patient and believe in possibility. Acceptance is no different. It's a path that I only recently set foot on; it unfolds before me every day as I learn to heal emotional wounds, work together with my body, and change my inner narrative. There is still a long way to go on this metaphorical mountain, but that's okay. As long as I am determined and continue taking steps to live as best as I can *with* endometriosis instead of constantly feeling like it's me *versus* endometriosis, I will one day find myself watching a beautiful sunrise from the top.

Self-Reflection

- Do you use military language around your illness, like combat, destroy, beat, battle, fight, warrior, or conquer?
- Do you feel like you fight against your illness and body, or do you work together with it? Or do you do both?
- To you, what is the difference?
- Do you think one is more tiring than the other?
- Do you think one is better for you personally than the other?
- Can you think of any times that you worked together with your body?

20

THE LANDSCAPE OF PAIN

Note: This essay contains descriptions of pain that some readers may find upsetting.

A creative writing piece on pain during sex.

In the middle of having sex, I am suddenly ripped away from my happiness to find myself lying alone and naked, transplanted to a destitute landscape. I'm surrounded by dirt and thorny shrubs, and the sky above is ominously black. There are no trees or shelter; I am out in the open and vulnerable.

Confused and startled, I try to get up, but the movement causes searing pain in my gut. I cry out in agony and realize I'm held to the ground by a long sword through my abdomen. The pain is excruciating, and I quickly give up struggling.

What's going on? Where am I?! I look around desperately. The barren earth stretches on endlessly. All of a sudden, daggers begin to fall from the sky. I gasp in shock and fear as the rainstorm of sharp blades comes hurtling down. One of them stabs me in my vagina, another in my side. All I can do is cover my face with my arms, breathe through the pain, and hope that it ends quickly.

When the worst of the storm passes, I try to make sense of this strange and unexpected situation. How do I get out of here? I had been lying with my partner in bed; we had been having fun, but now... here I am. I try to yell for help, but each breath pushes the sword deeper into my uterus. "Help!" It comes out as a whisper. I begin to panic. Since I am trapped down by the sword and can't get up, I crane my neck to see what's behind me.

There! I spot my partner on a distant hill, the sun shining over it. Baby bunnies are peacefully grazing on the green grass under the shade of a huge willow tree. He's sitting on a bench, enjoying the day, whistling happily without a care in the world. He is in paradise, in a completely different world than the hell I now find myself in.

"I'm here," I try to tell him. "Help me." He can't hear me. My lips are moving, but he doesn't notice. No sound is coming out. The pain has even stolen my voice. I slap my hand against the side of my bare leg, hoping the noise will get his attention.

He finally looks up from his paradise. "What? What's going on? Are you okay?!" He rushes down the hill, zigzagging around jagged rocks and boulders to reach me. He looks scared. "What is this place?" Severe pain can be very startling up close, even for someone that's seen it multiple times.

"I'm in pain," I whisper. He holds my hand, and we lie there quietly together. Hours go by. At some point, as the pain starts to fade, I find myself back in bed, breathing shallowly, completely still. I sigh with relief—the worst of it is over. I'm no longer in that cruel, harsh landscape of pain—for today at least.

Eventually, I need to go to the bathroom. My partner gently helps me stand. My face contorts in pain from the movement, and I pant and moan.

"I know, baby, I know," he says.

You don't know, I think. *You don't know this pain from another world. It can't be real.*

I inch my way down the hall from my bedroom to the bathroom, hunched over, avoiding the boulders and fallen daggers. My partner hovers close, unsure of what to do. A few long minutes later, I manage to walk the twenty feet down the hall to the bathroom. A wave of gratitude comes over me that I can now sit on the toilet and rest after such effort. I grit my teeth and scream out as my partner helps me bend down onto the toilet.

The night lasts an eternity. I hardly sleep at all from pain, but luckily, it's Saturday, and the next day we don't have to work. My partner lies on the far side of the bed, every now and then asking if he can hold my hand. "I'm afraid to touch you," he says. "I don't want to hurt you." I nod, almost imperceptibly. I must conserve all energy. I mustn't move a millimeter. Sunday morning drags out; the pain slowly begins to ebb. By Sunday afternoon, I can finally get to the bathroom by myself.

Twenty hours has gone by since I was dropped into that jolting, terrifying place. Thankfully, the sword has withdrawn from my uterus, and now I'm only left waiting for the gaping wound to heal. Thoughts begin to creep in. How can sharing an intimate moment with your partner—something beautiful and divine—turn into something so evil? It deeply disturbs me. I feel a heavy sadness in my soul; I feel as lifeless as the strewn daggers that I slowly begin to pick up from around my room, numbly dropping them into a large garbage bag. My chest tightens with anger. Why did it start hailing daggers like that? Why is life so painful and cruel?

No time to think about it now. I need to sleep; I work tomorrow at eight in the morning, and in spite of being bedridden all weekend, I haven't rested at all. I push aside my emotions, tie the garbage bag, and drop it to the side of my bed.

I will deal with you when I can, I think, as exhaustion takes over my body and I fade into a tormented sleep.

Self-Reflection

- Do you have pain during sex? If so, how does it make you feel?
- Think of your worst endometriosis symptom. What is so bad about it?
- Has anything in your life changed because you experience this?
- Has it made you feel isolated from the people you love?
- Take a moment to acknowledge your symptoms and to tell yourself it's okay to be upset about having them.

21

AM I A BURDEN?

"Do you mind walking to the printer and picking up my photocopies?" I ask my coworker, my face burning with shame—I'm in too much pain to leave my chair.

"Do you mind driving me to my colonoscopy appointment at 6 a.m.?" I ask my best friend, my stomach tensing and my heart pounding loudly.

"Can you help me get dressed?" I ask my partner, my heart weighed down by sadness as I think about how he has also become my caretaker, carrying me to the toilet during my worst pain flares, cleaning up my vomit, helping me with the littlest tasks when fatigue steals my energy.

What can I possibly say to them besides, "I'm so sorry you all have to help me and that I can't do these things myself."

The fear that I'm a burden is a poison leaching into my relationships with those around me—and with myself. This perception of myself has annihilated my self-esteem. I find myself saying "I'm sorry" more than a dozen times a day; I wonder constantly why my partner hasn't left me yet for someone who isn't so dependent and such a drain.

I'm so convinced that I'm a burden that I don't take seriously what my partner *actually* says to me. Although he reassures me that he's happy to help because he loves me, I doubt him and refuse to believe it. It's difficult to let in other people's caring and kindness. I feel an intrinsic unworthiness that I can't seem to shake off.

I have now spent enough time in meditation looking at my thoughts to recognize what this belief of "I am a burden" really is: another false story of self-sabotage that replays itself in my subconscious. It goes hand in hand with another story I have told myself for as long as I can remember: that I am not worthy of love. This is another disempowering lie I've reinforced to myself over years of being sick with thoughts like: "I'm going to end up alone;" "No one would ever love a person like me;" "I don't understand what he sees in me."

It's difficult to untangle myself from these beliefs, the patterns of which are deep within me. I keep reminding myself that these are just thoughts. Thinking something doesn't make that thought true or my identity, but having a chronic illness puts me in situations that make these thoughts seem like truths. As endometriosis pain and fatigue steal my ability at times to be independent, to help others, to do simple tasks that then have to fall on my loved ones, it provides 'evidence' of my long-held ideas that I'm a burden and unloveable.

One day during meditation, as I watched these thoughts flood my mind, I realized that the question isn't, *Am I a burden?* but rather, *Can I let in other people's love?* Can I let my partner help me without feeling me guilty? Can I let in the kindness of my friends without feeling like I'm draining them? It's okay to need help sometimes—it really is. Isn't that what we do for the people we love, and sometimes even for strangers? We reach our hands out to each other when we are in need. That is the one of the most beautiful qualities of humanity—our ability to care for and support one another. Don't I do the same for the people I care about?

Yes, I do. I've stayed late to help clean up my friend's dinner parties after all the guests left. I've sacrificed sleep to drive my partner to the airport at four in the morning so he can catch the early plane for his work trips. I've voluntarily shared the workload with coworkers when a big project got assigned to them so they wouldn't have to work overtime. I do this because I want to, because it makes me happy to help. Does helping them fill me with resentment or annoyance toward them? No. It dawned on me that this is exactly what people have told me as they assisted me with something related to my illness: "I'm happy to help."

Did the people I've helped feel ashamed, inadequate, or vulnerable when I helped them? I don't know, but I would hate to think that they did. My goal with helping them wasn't to make them feel terrible about themselves; rather, it was to show kindness to a person that I care about and help ease their load. So why do I feel so awful about the kindness that people show *me*?

If the roles were reversed and my partner or best friend had endometriosis, I wouldn't care if I had to clean up their vomit, drive them to doctors' appointments, or take on all the chores for two months while they recover from a surgery. Out of my love for them, I would do it all without thinking twice. Not because I deserve some kind of heroic medal, but because that's what people do for each other. So why don't I let them do that for me? Why do I consider myself a burden if I wouldn't see them as one?

It comes back to the stories I tell myself. My own thoughts are holding me hostage, preventing me from fully allowing others to show me kindness and love, and preventing me from experiencing the beauty of that love. When my partner supports me with my illness, it saddens me and makes me angry with myself instead of warming my heart that he loves me enough to support me. When I think about that, it saddens me to come to understand just how deeply my feelings of being undeserving run.

Time to let go of this well-ingrained, toxic story; I need to program a better one into my subconscious. We are all worthy of love—every single one of us. *This* is what I should be telling myself daily. It feels strange to say that I am worthy of love, but I know that is just because I am unaccustomed to seeing myself this way. The more I tell myself this truth, the more comfortable I will become with it.

May we learn to let go of these damaging stories we've carried for so long. May the edges of our hearts soften to let in love—including love toward ourselves.

Self-Reflection

- Do you feel you are a burden or a bother? Why do you feel that way?
- Is it easy for you to let in other people's love or kindness? Why or why not?
- Have you ever done a favor for a friend or a loved one?
- How did it make you feel to do it?
- How does the way you feel upon *giving* help compare to the way you feel upon *receiving* it?
- Are these feelings in contrast with each other?

22

MY PERSPECTIVE IS EVERYTHING

I look at the phrases scribbled on my notepad, random thoughts that came to my mind that I wanted to hold onto. One says, *Lifelong struggle.*

Who defines what a struggle is? Some people would say it's a struggle to climb Mount Everest; others would say it's an exhilarating adventure. What if I stop seeing my illness as a struggle and I just start seeing it as my life? Some people even see their illness as a gift. Will I ever see mine that way?

There are countless perspectives we can take on any given situation. We put labels, attachments, and emotions on circumstances and objects that in themselves have no value—*we* decide what they mean to us through the stories we tell ourselves about them.

Like the other day, when I found $10 on the sidewalk. To me, it was a surprising and positive moment, but to the person who lost that money, it was probably disappointing and upsetting. Yet, in reality, it was nothing more than a ten dollar bill lying on the sidewalk. The money itself was just there, an emotionless piece of paper. It was me (and likely the person that lost the money!) that was attaching meaning to it.

In fact, I could have thought about it in a completely different way. I could have been wracked with guilt that someone else had this misfortune of losing their money. Or maybe the person who lost it felt joy: "Well, I lost $10, but that's okay because whoever finds it is going to be really happy! So, actually, I made someone's day!"

Extending that to my friend, who I casually informed of my luck, the $10 had no meaning for her. "Good for you!" she said, then changed the topic.

The meaning of something is subject to interpretation and can change depending on who is assigning the value. This means that *anything* can have *any* meaning. The truth that I can assign all acts and events any meaning that I want has the power to be life-changing.

But currently, I'm not consciously assigning meaning to my circumstances. My feelings are mostly subconscious habits and lifelong conditioning. When I observe the thoughts that run through my mind, I can see that so many of the circumstances that make me angry, sad, or upset are actually neutral in themselves: the traffic, the weather, the crowd at the store. It is indeed my mind that is telling me stories about them.

I understand this, but in reality, it's challenging to let go of personal meaning, especially the meaning I assign to my illness. When I try to apply this same truth about assigning meaning—one that I am easily able to recognize with a ten dollar bill—to my endometriosis, that truth becomes hazy and harder to see. My feelings that my disease is ruining my life is rooted deep within me, and my thought patterns around my illness continue to reinforce those feelings.

Taking a step back from the thoughts, perspectives, and stories of meaning that I've built around my illness is no easy task. Whenever I have a flare, all kinds of emotional suffering arise with the physical pain. In my quest to have a better mindset about my disease, I've been reading Buddhist texts on suffering. One teaches that when something happens to us that causes us pain, it's like we are shot with an arrow—one that we cannot avoid; one shot by the universe. Depending on how we react to the first arrow, we may end up shooting ourselves with a second arrow—this is the arrow of suffering, and unlike the first arrow, it is optional.

Endometriosis is an example in my life of the first arrow. The stories I've built around it are the second arrow: stories of judgment and self-blame, stories of my 'bad luck' and being a victim, stories of exaggeration and doom.

When I notice myself placing one of these arrows in my bow, I'm now trying to pause and change the narrative in my mind before I automatically shoot myself with it:

Yes, I'm in a flare, but...
This isn't a punishment.
This isn't my fault.
This isn't 'just one more thing' going wrong in my life.
This isn't an example of my terrible bad luck.
This doesn't mean I will never feel better.
I'm not being singled out; suffering is universal.

I assign all kinds of meaning to my flares. But in reality? They are just flares. The pain, digestive problems, and fatigue are physiological responses in the body to tissue that shouldn't be there, tissue that can destabilize the surrounding capillaries causing bleeding and the formation of scar tissue. The biology of the human body is incredibly complex, and my flares are a natural reaction to the endometriosis lesions, organs fusing together, and inflammation.

Yet in my mind, that's not what's happening. My mind is playing out a story of guilt, low self-worth, and victim mentality ("Why me?!"). It's attached all kinds of personal meaning to neutral circumstances of biology that really have nothing to do with me on an emotional level. As it currently stands, I never run out of arrows to shoot myself with, and I've become so adept at shooting them that I just automatically reach for them when there's a flare present.

But you know what? I don't have to shoot myself with the second arrow nor attach meaning to my endometriosis. Endometriosis just is. It's endometriosis. It's not proof of what a terrible person I am; it's not an indicator that I'm doomed. It just is.

It's astounding how my perceptions can paint my reality. Finding ten dollars can be interpreted as a happy or sad event. Having endometriosis pain can be seen as bad luck, a consequence of biology, or a punishment from the universe. Which do I want to believe?

Can I keep learning how to pay attention to my thoughts and beliefs? To the stories I tell myself? To the personal meaning that I subconsciously attach to my circumstances? Can I shift my perspective to be more neutral about the things I hate? Can I cultivate more awareness so that I'll be able to return the drawn arrow to its quiver before I shoot myself with it?

Self-Reflection

- Do you like the rain? Why do you feel this way?
- Now, think about how you would feel about the rain if you were a farmer. Imagine there was a terrible drought and all the crops you and your family are depending on for food are dying from lack of water. How would you feel if it started raining?
- Now, imagine how you would feel if there were so much rain it caused the riverbanks to overflow and flood your home.

- Now, imagine how you would feel if you were outside in the middle of a field with no umbrella and it started raining.
- Now, imagine how you would feel if the rain were toxic and you were outside in the middle of a field with no umbrella when it started raining.
- Did each situation make you feel differently about the rain?
- Do you believe that we put our own personal meaning on everything that happens to us?
- Think of something you have recently put personal meaning on, something that you decided you disliked (but not hated). Write "I disliked _________." (For example, sitting in traffic, washing my laundry, that recent work project.)
- Now, write the opposite sentence about it. "I liked _________." (Sitting in traffic, washing my laundry, that recent work project.) Think of a reason why and write it down. "Because __________." (For example, I got to listen to the radio longer / I finally had clean underwear / I got to practice my excel skills.)
- See if you can practice putting a different meaning on the things you dislike to try to feel differently or more neutral about them.

23

ACCEPTANCE IS NOT LINEAR

It amazes me how often I feel like a failure, especially when it has to do with endometriosis. I'm trying to accept having this disease and live the best life I can with it, but I still so often get frustrated about some aspect of having it (like having to cancel plans due to a flare or not sleeping all night due to pain). I have to constantly remind myself that I'm not failing at accepting endometriosis. It's not that one day we learn a new concept and from that day forward, we will be perfect at it. There is no perfection on this path but rather a process of continuous growth. That's why techniques like mindfulness, self-compassion, and gratitude are called *practices*. The more we practice, the better we get at integrating these techniques into our lives and calling them forward in our times of crisis. That's also why it's common to use language around them that refers to gardening: *growing* our capacity for joy, *planting the seed* of gratitude, *cultivating* meaning, the *path* of acceptance. We are continuously learning and increasing our knowledge.

Acceptance is an ongoing journey; the path of acceptance is what we walk as we practice embracing the world as it is. Sometimes, it's full of fallen trees, huge potholes, and flowers that prick us with their thorns if we try to smell them. Other times, it's a place of beautiful sunrises, stunning mountain views, and a tranquil silence that can fill our soul.

Over the marathon of life, we are walking forward, but in short sprints, we might be walking backwards, sideways, or even in circles. One day, we might be able to look at a picture from our past and allow it to fill us with a happy nostalgia—what a fun music festival that was! On another day, looking at that same picture might depress us—it really sucks that I'm too sick to go to music festivals with friends like I used to. Both reactions are perfectly okay. To cry today at something that we thought we were done crying over doesn't make us a failure—it makes us human. Acceptance is a gradual *process* of learning, changing, and adapting that is different for all of us, but each day our experiences are moving us a step closer. Acceptance is something that unfolds in front of us and evolves *with* us. It changes us and changes with us. As time passes, we will be able to see how far we have come.

Let's be gentle with ourselves on the path of acceptance. No judging ourselves for how long we think we're taking or for our supposed 'regressions'; no comparing ourselves to others and where they are, nor where we think we should be. No more expectations. Wherever we are is where we are—and that's okay. Let's give ourselves permission to be there. If we are still enraged at endometriosis, that's okay. If we are still grieving our old life, that's okay, too. If we want to give up on acceptance today and try again tomorrow, that's okay, too.

A huge triumph for me was just stepping onto this path. For years and years, acceptance once seemed completely out of reach to me. My breath would go shallow and my hands would tighten into fists if anyone dared to suggest I try to accept this terrible disease. Although I was miserable, my mind was very comfortable in my bitter relationship with my endometriosis. I was stuck in my anger and sadness—it felt like it was my nature and that I would never feel differently. But it turned out that in order to *feel* differently, I had to *do* something differently.

Now, at the thought of acceptance, my lips pull up in a slight smile. My resistance around the idea has dissolved, the hardened edges of my heart have softened. My mind finally has grown comfortable with the idea of acceptance, and that allowed me to step onto this winding, frightening yet beautiful path, to see where it will take me. Acceptance isn't a place where I am yet, but it is a place where I am going.

In an unbelievably short amount of time, the mindset practices I've started—meditating to step back and observe my thoughts instead of being lost in them, changing my self-talk to be kind to myself, and taking a minute to name three reasons daily why I am grateful—have begun to transform my life. I was not expecting that at all, let alone so quickly. And this has had a ripple effect that I never could have imagined. These small steps are positively affecting my self-esteem, my confidence, my thought patterns, my decisions, my job, my relationships, my mood—because everything is connected.

There are still days I stumble, but that's just part of the process. There are days I'm too busy to meditate; other days I just can't motivate myself. There are days spent in so much pain that I can't think of three reasons I am grateful. Usually, by the end of those days, my mood worsens and my frustration with having this disease begins to come back a little bit more. But all I can do is say, "I'll try again tomorrow." And as long as I'm trying, I'm moving forward, even if it doesn't always feel like it.

Self-Reflection

- What does your path to acceptance look like, if you were to describe it? Is it a garden path, a river, a highway?

- What do the obstacles on it look like?
- When you imagine yourself on it, are you always moving forward or are you ever stuck or 'regressing'?
- Think of a time that you felt like you've gotten stuck or 'regressed'. For example, you realized you weren't over something you thought you were, or you were unable to apply something you thought you had learned, like patience or forgiveness. What happened?
- Now look at it from another point of view: did being stuck or 'regressing' actually strengthen your practice? For example, did it make you recommit, understand that you need to explore the topic further, or realize that it is okay not to be perfect?

24

A LUCKY COINCIDENCE

A memory from college.

My symptoms continued to get worse. My parents took me to various doctors searching for an answer, but no one knew what was wrong with me. A few weeks into the summer vacation before my third year of college, I got a lead. A specialist in infectious diseases discovered that my blood test showed high levels of antibodies to the Epstein-Barr virus.

Epstein-Barr is the virus that causes mononucleosis (also known as mono or glandular fever). It's very common, and most adults will test positive for the antibodies to it. The doctor didn't think that this was the cause of my problems, but he did remark that it was strange that I had *such* extremely high counts of Epstein-Barr antibodies in my blood.

Like all the other doctors, he said he didn't know how to help me. This time, though, I didn't mind. I actually felt excited—a feeling I hadn't felt in a long, long time. This was the first time in two years that everything hadn't come back negative. Colonoscopies, endoscopies, allergy tests, neurological tests, laparoscopic surgery—they kept finding that I was in 'excellent' health.

"I got a name for something!" I told my *Get well soon* troll doll in the car after the appointment. "Can you believe it?! Finally, a test that didn't come back as normal! My first clue in two years to whatever is going on with my body! This might be the reason why I'm so tired all the time."

On my drive home, I stopped for a minute at the thrift store, one of my favorite pastimes. Heading toward the shoe section, I passed by a huge pile of books in a box on the floor. The bright red block letters of the one on top caught my eye: it was a book on overcoming the Epstein-Barr virus.

I picked up the book for a closer look, and right beneath it, there was another book on beating chronic fatigue. It felt like fate. I never would have given that top book a thought had I seen it the day before. Yesterday, the words 'Epstein-Barr virus' meant nothing to me. Today, it was the one lead I had about my health—my only clue to what might be wrong. And here was a guide on how to heal from it, as if it were waiting for me.

I bought the two books for fifty cents each and rushed back to my car, eager to get home and start reading them right away. I placed them on the front seat, next to my dolly.

"Look!" I showed her, so excited I was practically shouting. "These books explain about how I can overcome Epstein-Barr and chronic fatigue! Can you believe my luck?! They teach you how to help yourself. Isn't this amazing?"

Those books were my first introduction to the idea that the way I live and what I eat matters in how I feel. Looking through the different chapters, I quickly realized that I wanted to learn everything I could about the Epstein-Barr virus, along with hormones, nutrition, and the body. The doctors kept saying they didn't know how to help me, and that had me feeling terrified, confused, and lost. Right at the time when I was losing hope that I would ever feel better, those books helped me see that maybe I could do more for myself than I thought. Maybe I did have a chance at actually feeling better.[1]

The diet and lifestyle changes I made over the next few years really added up. Through continuous education about how certain foods and habits can effect the body, as well as trial and error to see what actually worked for me, I found ways to manage some (although not all) of my symptoms and take back pieces of my life from the claws of endometriosis. My health stopped feeling completely out of my control, and I gained a new sense of hope and empowerment.

Self-Reflection

- Have you had any pivotal or *Aha!* moments in relation to your illness?
- Have you found any ways to empower yourself in your illness? For example, have you changed your diet, researched about the disease, joined a support group?
- If you have found a way to empower yourself, how did you feel when you first learned about this new thing or decided to begin doing it?
- If you haven't found any ways to empower yourself in your illness, can you think of any places to start?

25

LIVING UNDER A BROKEN SKY

"Why me?" How much my mind loves to ask that question, which is funny because I'm one of 200,000,000+ worldwide with endometriosis and among 7,700,000,000+ people suffering in some way or another on this planet. Billions of people are getting ill, having misfortunes, and losing loved ones. Why do I think I should be immune to suffering? I know that I am not any better or different than the rest of the individuals that make up humanity. But it still seems unbelievable that anything could happen to anyone at any time, including to me.

It was shocking and astounding when I first got sick, but it's been a decade since the onset of my illness. Why am I still holding onto this idea that *my* life isn't supposed to be like this? That this wasn't supposed to happen to me?

Perhaps the real question I should be asking myself is "Why *not* me?" I have endometriosis—and it's awful—but there are endless tragedies and challenges I could also be facing. Life, for all of us, is full of problems, like that game Whack-A-Mole that I played in the arcade when I was a kid. A mole pops up. You whack it down. Another pops up in a different spot. You whack it down. And another. You hit it. And again. And again. Just like with this game and the moles, life's problems pop up, sometimes one after another, sometimes tiny and sometimes enormous. Problems are a part of life—of all of our lives. And yet, because of my subconscious belief that suffering shouldn't happen to me, I've interpreted my share of life's universal hardships as a personal vendetta of the universe against me.

Whenever I have a flare, it rocks my world and the sky starts falling in from my injustice at it happening to *me*. But billions of people around the world live under broken pieces of sky. I'm starting to wake up from my imagined reality for myself, to see the truth that life is full of unpredictability and impermanence. My life is no exception. There are troubles and tragedies in life which can be deeply painful, and having this disease is one of mine. It's important I take the time to grieve how I wanted my life to be, but it's just as important that I take the time to come to terms with what's happened and heal. In this way, I can eventually move forward.

I have found my answer to the burning question of *Why me?* It's not just me—it's me, you, that person, that other person, *all of us*, because suffering is universal and a part of being human.

Self-Reflection

Do you think that suffering is universal? Sit for a minute with this idea—really, simply sit down and think about it. What do you feel? Does it make you feel angry or sad that people worldwide are facing difficult moments? Relieved that you aren't alone in your suffering? Grateful for what is going right in your life?

Let's practice bringing loving-kindness to yourself and to those suffering. Put your hand on your heart and acknowledge your suffering. Say something about your situation, such as, "I am in pain / This is a difficult moment / This is a moment of suffering / Endometriosis makes my life challenging."

Breathe in deeply. Exhale. Now, without diminishing your own suffering, think about someone else that is suffering. This could be a loved one, a friend, or a group of people who you heard about on the news. Gently say something like: "This person is suffering too / Suffering is universal / Suffering is the human condition / I'm not alone in my suffering / 200 million people have endometriosis and suffer with me."

What do you wish for yourself in your suffering? Say it out loud. For example, "May I be strong / Give me the courage I need to get through this / Please let me figure out how to get through this."

Now, bring back to your mind the person / people suffering that you thought about a minute ago. Wish them the same qualities to get through their suffering: "May they be strong / Give them the courage they need to get through this / Please let them figure out how to get through this."

Do you like or dislike this activity? Why? What feelings came up as you did it?

26

THE WISDOM OF AN ITCH

What I would do to just be comfortable in my body, even for a few minutes! If it isn't the nausea, it's the gnawing hunger that comes after having diarrhea. If it's not a hot flash, it's the chills. If it's not my arms tingling for hours, it's the dull ache in my legs or the crushing pressure in my back. If it isn't the heaviness in my eyelids from fatigue, it's the migraine. With diet and lifestyle changes, I no longer have *all* of these symptoms every single day, but I still have a few on good days and several on bad days. No matter what I do, I can't find relief from my endometriosis.

What can one do but learn to endure it? Vipassana meditation (a technique that teaches self-observation and awareness, training a person to sit with the sensations in their body to gain insight into themselves) has been such a gift in this regard. This type of meditation has been teaching me how to be with the sensations in my body and stay present to them—to accept the discomfort of the aches, migraines, and hot flashes and not let thinking about those discomforts rule me. Through Vipassana, I've been able to take back control of my thoughts around my symptoms, which helps immensely with how I feel *emotionally* throughout the day. I'm less upset by my pain, less angered, less frustrated, less reactive, and more neutral and at peace with how I physically feel.

Practicing this started off small—could I have an itch and simply learn to let it be instead of scratching it? Normally, I would immediately and mindlessly scratch any itch that arose, without even realizing that I was doing that. But when practicing Vipassana, I refrain from scratching. I still remember the first time I did this. Not alleviating the itch only intensified the itching sensation, as well as my urge to scratch. But (with great difficulty) I still didn't scratch it. Rather, I noticed it—how torturous the itch became, how it moved across my back, my overwhelming desperation to scratch it. I noticed how I started to judge the itch, telling myself how awful it was. I hated it. I wanted to be rid of it. I even started to worry—what if it's actually a bug crawling on my back? I needed to scratch it. I needed to!

I watched all of my thoughts unfolding while sitting still and silent. Finally, I couldn't resist any longer. The itch took control of me and I absolutely had to scratch it, so I did, frantically and wildly rubbing my fingers over the skin. Ahhh, the relief!

As the panic of the itch subsided, I noticed how a heaviness appeared on my shoulders as feelings of being a failure at meditating came in. But I've also been working on self-compassion, so I took a few deep, slow breaths as I consciously brought in feelings of kindness and understanding toward myself, and acknowledged my tendency for self-criticism.

Today, after several days of practicing for a few minutes daily, I managed to sit with an itch all the way through without scratching. It was amazing to witness how the itch eventually disappeared just as spontaneously and suddenly as it arose. It went from torturing me to magically vanishing, as if it never existed at all. I smiled to myself, proud of my achievement—I had successfully waited for the itch to pass. I'd succeeded at Vipassana meditation!

Then, I noticed my language: 'achievement' and 'succeeded.' If I end up scratching a future itch, will I tell myself a story about how I am a disappointment or about how I regressed in my practice? Meditation is not about being perfect or hitting a goal, like 'ten itches not scratched this week!' Actually, that's the opposite of what meditation is. Meditation is not about striving, doing, achieving, or going after something. There's no 'achieving' nor is there 'failing' in meditation; if I scratch or don't scratch my itch today, then that's just my experience.

What meditation is about is cultivating nonjudgmental awareness of my thoughts, circumstances, and body sensations. While I initially thought I was learning not to scratch an itch, what I am *actually* learning is how to be with whatever comes up. Giving in to scratching an itch isn't 'bad'—it presents an opportunity to see what arises in me physically and emotionally when I do. It's incredible how much a person can learn about the nature of the universe, and also themselves, by observing an itch and the thoughts that run through their mind as they try not to scratch it.

I can see my need to be in control: "I *have* to scratch it."
I can see my tendency toward self-criticism: "I'm a disappointment for scratching it."
I can see my mind's love for worrying and making up stories: "There might be a bug on my back!"
I can see how my mind loves to want: "I want to scratch it—no, I *need* to scratch it."
I can see the role my mind plays in my suffering: it wants to run away from the unpleasant, and when it can't, I suffer—when I don't stop the itching, I'm miserable.

I can also see the impermanent nature of my body sensations: the itch will disappear just as randomly as it arises. The more I practice sitting with my body, watching the sensations as they come and go, the more I'm aware that my pain flares are exactly the same. Yes, they last much longer than an itch. Yes, they are much more intense; often I'm not able to sit still through the pain—instead, I'm thrashing about or vomiting. Yet, like the itch, the pain eventually passes. Like the itch, I can learn not to get swept up by my feelings toward the pain. Like the itch, I can learn to observe the pain neutrally without judging it or my reactions to it as good nor bad. The pain will be there regardless, so I am going to try to learn to have it without letting it rule my thoughts. As I apply the teachings of Vipassana meditation toward my pain, I find that although I can't change the intensity of the pain, I can improve my ability to tolerate it.

Self-Reflection

Find ten minutes where you won't be disturbed. Sit or lie down in a quiet place, and begin to scan how your body feels from head to toe, staying with each area of the body for two to three breaths. First, focus your awareness on your forehead. What sensations do you feel there? Do you have an itch, pain, tingling, tension, cold, heat? Can you feel the sensation of the air on your skin? Practice noticing your sensations as a neutral observer, without looking for relief from them, hating them, or wanting them to stay longer if they are pleasant. Just notice how your body feels. Remember that this is just a practice—if you find yourself getting distracted, it's okay. Just bring your attention back to your body.

Now pass your awareness to your mouth, staying there for a few breaths, and noting any sensations. Continue noting what you feel in your body as you move your awareness to the back of your head, then to your neck, to your left shoulder, left upper arm, left lower arm, left hand, then left fingers. Then move to scan your right arm the same way, slowly working from your shoulder to your fingers. Move to your chest, stomach, upper back, lower back, left hip, left thigh, left knee, left calf, left ankle, left foot, left toes, then move on to scan your right leg.

This is a great practice to do once a day for fifteen minutes to start being in tune nonjudgmentally with what you are feeling in your body.

27

THE FLEETING LIFE OF A LILAC

I got news this morning that my friend passed away. She had late stage stomach cancer, so we knew this day was coming, but my heart feels heavy. I know I should feel sad, but the only thing I am is numb.

I leave for work, walking along my usual route to the train station and passing by a large lilac bush that had bloomed with hundreds of purple flowers a few weeks ago. Every day, I'd been getting a whiff of their sweet aroma in the breeze, and I would stop and press my nose into the petals, inhaling deeply.

The beauty of a lilac is short-lived. Just a few days ago, the flowers had started wilting and falling off the bush. Yesterday, there were more flowers on the ground below than actually on the branches, and how befitting that today, as if commemorating my friend, there are no more lilacs on the bush. Only a few purple flowers are squished into the dirt below; they are all that remain after the rest were washed away in last night's thunderstorms.

The bush is green again, devoid of its lilacs, but the tree next to it is starting to bloom, its branches covered in tiny pink buds. One flower wilts, another blooms. Each has its moment, and like the purple lilac, it's no longer my friend's moment. She is gone; where, I don't know, but she has gone from the world that I presently live in.

Did the lilacs have a sense of time as they hung from the branches, soaking up the sun and swaying in the breeze, their scent filling the air around them? Did they cry as their petals began to fall off the bush? Did they know their life on this earth was limited?

Life. We only get one chance at it. I suddenly feel panicked; my friend's death is sinking in and jolts me, reminding me that I will not live forever. One day, my body will disappear, just as these lilacs did. I will become part of the dirt of the earth and the dust in the air.

As I look at the few remaining lilacs lying lifeless on the ground, I am once more reminded that I have been running through life without not paying the slightest attention to the beauty around me. I have lost the happiness that we all once knew as innocent babies, the enchantment with the world that often gets buried under heavy weights on our shoulders called Responsibility, Work, Obligation, and Growing Up. Mine has been further buried under the burdens called Chronic Illness and Pain.

I have been missing the joy and the magic right in front of me all this time. This morning, perhaps because of my friend's death, I am acutely aware of the eternal life-force that runs through all living things. I can feel its presence in the pink flowers budding on the bush before me, in the trees growing tall toward the sky with their branches casting intricate shadows on the ground, and in myself as I breathe in the sweet smell of the spring flowers. Some call this life-force miraculous, mysterious, or divine. Whatever it is, it's always there, in all living things from the grandest to the tiniest.

Why is it so easy to lose sight of this?

I pick up one of the lilacs from the ground. It's been flattened and crushed. I bring it to my nose, but it no longer has any scent. It's dead—and so is my friend. My breath catches in my throat. Looking at this squashed, broken lilac in my hand, I can feel the impermanence of life. I place the lilac gently on the ground and continue walking to the train station.

If I were to die today, how would I feel about my life? Sad. Cheated. Disappointed. Aware that in spite of the fragility of life, I have spent an extraordinary amount of time wishing my life away instead of living it. There were countless days that I had wished I were at home instead of at work, wished it were the weekend, wished I were already on vacation, wished I weren't in the bathroom again, wished to be somewhere else other than where I was. How many hours, days, and months have I put my energy into wishing away the time instead of being present? Inevitably, death will arrive for me. I want to take my last breath knowing that I didn't squander my time on this earth—that I lived fully and made an effort to find meaning.

In the months leading up to my friend's death, she slowed her life down and told me that by doing so, life no longer seemed to be racing by. I watched the happiness she found as she became more present. Although she was approaching the end of her life, with each day her eyes seemed more radiant than ever. Her physical body was dying, but on an emotional level she was healing through the work she was doing to stay open and aware.

I, too, am taking steps to try to forgive, accept, and live wholeheartedly. My friend found peace in the face of death, and she is one of many humans on this earth who have managed to do so. We may not be able to defy the limitations of our body, but we can indeed lift the limitations on our hearts and minds to heal on an emotional level.

Self-Reflection

- If you were to pass away tomorrow, how would you feel toward the life you've lived until now? Would you be satisfied with it, or would you have regrets?
- Have you wished much of your life away? Why have or haven't you done that?
- What has your relationship been with your life?
- Has that relationship been constant or has it changed over time?
- Do you think it's possible to change your relationship with your life? Do you want to?
- Do you know anyone who has found peace in the face of illness or death?

28

RESCUED BY A CANDLE

I look around the apartment. When I'm in a weeklong flare, the dust builds up quickly, the dishes even quicker. Laundry overflows out of the basket; the toilet is streaked with dried period blood.

I cringe at how my filth is accumulating. My house is a mess—just like I am. Am I failing at life? "Self-judgment. Self-judgment." I name out loud my thought pattern, enabling me to take a step back and remind myself that I don't have to be perfect. I can clean up when I feel better.

But when will that be? I'm going through the motions—work, grocery store, home, repeat—but inside, I feel empty. Right now, there's no joy in my life. My soul is withering away, drying and shrinking, like a sponge that isn't being used. I know I have to find little moments of meaning. Again and again, I've told myself to be present, to find a reason to smile, to appreciate the little things, and find reasons that make my bleak existence worthwhile. But when I have an endometriosis flare, all those meaningful moments seem to disappear. For example, the nausea strips all flavor from my usually delicious homemade breakfast cocoa balls; I have to force myself to choke them down. While normally I find taking a walk relaxing, tossing and turning all night from pain turns my beloved morning walk into torture.

With endometriosis, so much of what gives me joy feels inaccessible. I'm often too fatigued to go out into nature or on a weekend getaway (despite how much I'd love to relax!). Money is tight with medical bills adding up—another limitation on what activities I can do. I can't indulge myself with a glass of wine or chocolate ice cream without having a flare. Pampering myself with mud masks and beauty products isn't possible—I've developed a sensitivity to chemicals and even most natural products. Not to mention, where can I find good moments when my period comes and I'm in agonizing pain? What can I appreciate when my bowel is spasming violently and my uterus is contracting? Sometimes, I feel trapped in this body and in this life I am stuck living.

When a flare hits me, life starts to become a blur, a chore, an obligation—nothing but sickness and pain. But those are the days when I really need to be awake to what's happening around me, when I truly need to notice the warmth of the shower, the comfort of a loved one's hug, or how a good book can bring me on an adventure. Currently, a week of pain has put me in a state of fatigue and apathy that has completely drained my motivation to do anything that could revitalize me; yet ironically, doing something meaningful would break me free from this sadness that has swallowed me up. Sometimes, I feel like I'm fighting not to be numb to the meaning that is around me. I recognize that being numb isn't where I want to be but struggle to seek out something that provides me joy.

Think, Amy, think... What can you do to help yourself right now? Ideas run through my head, but none of them are appealing. I'm in too much pain to care. I lie on the bed, staring up at the ceiling fan. It brings forth memories of living in the rainforest—how often I had stared up at the ceiling in my hut and wished I had a ceiling fan to provide a breeze from the stifling heat! But there were no fans in the rainforest, nor was there electricity, phones, or TV. In the evenings, there was nothing else to do except visit the huts of the other villagers. Over their fire, we would cook plantains and simply enjoy each other's company. I miss this pastime of staring into bright orange flames. Hours dissolved away as I watched the embers' deep red glow. Without words, the fire would speak to me through the calm and steady smoldering of the wood it consumed, telling me stories of belonging and the beginning of time. Campfires can be incredibly hypnotic and mesmerizing.

Suddenly, I have an idea! I rummage around one of the bathroom drawers and find what I am looking for—a wide pillar candle, ivory in color. I shut off all the lights, place the candle in front of me, and put on soothing music.

The feeling in my apartment immediately changes. The flame dances on its wick; its orange flicker provides a soft glow and a sense of peace. With this calmer atmosphere, my heart feels less suffocated by the emptiness that has been weighing down on it. My little candle 'campfire' is a literal light in the dark, encouraging me to simply be here—not be off in my head thinking about the pain or the stress the pain causes—simply here, sitting in the dark on my floor. In a strange way, I can breathe again.

These are the moments I have been desperately missing in my life—moments where I can take a breath. "Thank you," I say quietly to the candle. I am more and more convinced that simplicity is one of the keys to happiness. Finding a moment to breathe, learning how to clear my mind—I need this to feel more balanced before the crushing burden of my illness.

This candle has been a surprising lifeboat that has rescued

me from another long, lonely night. I smile slightly. I feel like myself again. It may only be while this candle flame dances before me, but it's something. "I'm still here," I say quietly to myself. "I'm okay."

I can see the outline of a clean pile of laundry that I still haven't put away. I walk over and begin slowly folding it. With my sight limited by the darkness of the room, I can feel the softness of the towels on my hands and how the texture of the sheets vary from one set to another. For a few minutes, I forget about the difficult week I've had and slip into a calm state of relaxation. I breathe slowly and deeply, watching how the shadow of my laundry changes as the candle flickers.

As the warmth of this quiet moment fills my heart, I realize that there really is a wide variety of ways to experience 10,000 joys, as Buddha taught. The trick is being present to the moment that you are in; otherwise, you can easily miss one of life's many simple opportunities for joy.

Self-Reflection

Take a few minutes to sit in a mostly darkened room. If you have a candle and can safely light it, do so. If not, sit with just a nightlight, the light from a window, or even simply your phone's flashlight pointing toward the ceiling. Look around the room. What changes when the lights are off? Notice the outlines of the furniture around you and the different shadows that are cast in the low light.

Is there any change in how you feel? Does the darkness make you feel calm, uncomfortable, restless, bored, at peace, sleepy? Before turning back on the light, allow those feelings for a few minutes, noticing them without judging them.

Can you think of any other simple act you can do for just a few minutes to be present in the moment? What allows you to take a calming breath and momentarily be at peace or forget about your difficulties? Besides watching a candle in the dark, examples could be sitting on a swing, walking down a nature path, taking ten minutes to color in a coloring book. If you can, try making this a daily habit. After a week, notice if you feel any different and/or look forward to your quiet moment.

29

WHAT IS LIFE ASKING OF ME?

There are nine small scars on my belly from three surgeries for endometriosis. A tenth, longer scar is from the removal of a grapefruit-sized endometrioma and my left ovary.

I trace my finger over the white, raised lines, easily contrasted against my olive skin. Like a map of my illness, these scars tell a story. At first, they were the story of the incompetence of the medical system, which resulted in the long delay in my diagnosis. In these scars, I saw the first exploratory laparoscopy I had at nineteen and the lack of training the average gynecologist has in endometriosis, resulting in that doctor assuring me that I didn't have this disease—when I did. In these scars, I saw the second surgery for the giant endometrioma that stole my left ovary and put me into perimenopause at thirty-four years old. Would the twelve centimeter cyst have grown that large if it weren't for the pervasive sex and gender bias in medicine that negatively impacts womxn's[1] care? If any of the several doctors who told me that I was exaggerating my pain, that period pain was normal, or that my brutal pain was 'in my head' had actually just taken me seriously, could it have been caught earlier?

These scars are a part of me. I see them every single day: when I look in the mirror, get dressed, shower. Do I want them to constantly cause me such angst about those infuriating obstacles to diagnosis? I don't. So instead, I'm now reframing the story these scars tell about me: a story that started sixteen years ago of my tenacity in advocating for myself to get my debilitating pain taken seriously. A story of my body's incredible ability to heal itself after two major surgeries. Of my strength to have gotten through hundreds of incapacitating pain flares. Of how I'm learning to love my body and myself in all of its imperfection and perceived 'brokenness.' Of my courage in the face of all of the uncertainty and changes that illness has brought me. Of my ability to get through the unbearable.

My scars are reminders of how much I've learned and how much I've grown. They are evidence of my resilience. My strength. My determination.

They are a reminder of my darkest storms—and how I stepped up to the challenges and overcame them all.

Self-Reflection

- If you have any scars due to your illness, what do you see when you look at them? What do they mean to you?
- What has the adversity you faced in your life asked of you? For example, have your challenges asked you to be strong, determined, resilient, or accepting?
- Focus on one quality that life has asked of you that you came through on. What was the situation?
- How does it make you feel to look back and know

that you stepped up to the challenge? Are you proud of yourself? Surprised? Impressed?

- Can you hold that feeling to keep building a reserve of knowledge of your own self-worth?

30

TRAPPED BETWEEN A LION AND A CLIFF

I'm losing hope. It's been two weeks of intense cramping, fatigue, and nausea. The first day of my period, the pain was too unbearable to move. The days since have been agony, but I went to work anyway, my abdomen burning, walking as slowly as a turtle, slightly hunched over from the pain. I sat at my desk with my heating pad on, not moving an inch except my fingers to type.

Tears streamed down my face when I was alone in my work cubicle; the effort to keep it together during conference calls was exhausting. Whenever a coworker looked in my direction, I'd slowly plaster a weak smile on my face. *I'm perfectly fine*, the smile would lie. Don't be fooled by the heating pad, my hunched posture, the dark eye circles, and the blanket I'm wrapped in—there is nothing happening with me, really. They would look away awkwardly, and I'd be free to slump back over my desk and wipe the tears from my eyes.

It's breaking me to muster up the strength to act like everything is fine when I actually want to curl up in a ball and cry. I could have called out of work, but to call out for a whole week?

If I did that each month—every time I had this level of pain—I would lose my job due to all my absences. Then what would I do? So over the years, I've learned to push myself more and more, increasing my limits of tolerance and enduring severe symptoms with a strength and a willpower that truly baffles me at times. The question I've been asking myself more and more these last few months is, *how did I survive today?*

I'm ecstatic today is Saturday, and I can be home, away from the pressure of pretending. My periods are getting worse each month, the debilitating cramps lasting for days, yet each time I can take fewer painkillers than before. Heartburn, stomach pain, and the other side effects of NSAIDs (nonsteroidal anti-inflammatory drugs) compounded with my recent diagnosis of gastritis makes taking any painkiller in this category hurt almost as much as the endometriosis pain I take them for.

Taking NSAIDs is the *only* way I've found to somewhat relieve the crushing endometriosis pain. Other types of painkillers (prescription or not) do nothing for my pain at all. Nor does birth control. Over the years, I tried different kinds: the shot, the ring, the patch, various pills. Most didn't help my period pain, and the few that did brought side effects, especially to my mental health, that didn't outweigh the benefits. As for the anti-inflammatory diet and lifestyle that has improved my day-to-day symptoms, it has done nothing for my period pain.

I need NSAIDs. I'm barely surviving right now, and that's *with* being able to take them. I only want to take them a few times a month; is that asking too much? Just to escape the invisible sledgehammer of endometriosis that slams into my back, breaking it in half like a piece of cement crumbling into rubble. That pain rips my soul apart. I *need* these painkillers.

Fear begins to creep in. There is no happiness right now, no beauty in my life. Everything seems depressing, drab, and confining. I wake up in pain, get dressed in pain, drive to work in pain, arrive at the office in pain, answer my emails in pain, arrive home in pain.

I can't do it; I can't keep this mask on my face any longer. I'm in pain! Does anybody care? Can anyone hear me crying? Standing at the counter, I look around the kitchen. The fridge hums, a red light on the dishwasher blinks, the microwave clock is an hour behind because I never reset it for daylight savings time. I am alone, and I begin to talk out loud to myself, to the fridge, to the clock. "I need those painkillers. I need them!"

Desperation overcomes me, and I collapse onto the floor, covering my face with my hands and sobbing loudly. What should I do? I feel like an animal, trapped between a lion and a cliff.

Lion: Take NSAIDs and avoid brutal endometriosis pain but get ripped apart by severe gastrointestinal side effects that last for a week, make it impossible to eat, and are almost as intolerable as the pain they alleviate.

Cliff: Don't take NSAIDs—which means suffering no side effects—but fall into the dark abyss of the brutal endometriosis pain, screaming, writhing, and vomiting for several hours.

Lion or cliff.

Both choices are awful, and I don't know what to do.

Self-Reflection

- Have you ever felt like you were stuck in your management options for your symptoms?
- Have you ever tried a medicine to relieve your symptoms, but the side effects were difficult to deal with?

- How did that make you feel emotionally? Were you frustrated, angry, or sad?
- Have you tried any natural ways to manage symptoms, like an anti-inflammatory diet, exercise, Traditional Chinese Medicine, supplements? Has that helped any?

31

REACH FOR MY HAND

Note: This essay contains descriptions of pain that some readers may find upsetting.

This black hole of pain is consuming me. All I can do is try to survive until the barbed wire squeezing my abdomen decides it has tortured me enough.

Who is that person moaning uncontrollably? Who is wailing in pain? Is that me?

There is no light here. No happiness. No hope. Relentless pain traps your soul and you don't know if you will ever find a way out.

I see a girl down there. She is just a shadow among the blackness, thrashing about in pain and gasping for air.

"Can you hear me?" I yell down into the hole. "Hold on. I see you in there. I see you."

I start talking to her, to let her know someone else is with her.

"It's impossible to pull you out of there—only time can save you. But I can be with you right now. I'm reaching for your hand. There. Can you feel me squeeze your hand? Can you feel the warmth of my skin? I know the pain is ruthless, but I'm here with you. You're not alone."

I hear her whimper from within the dark hole. I can't tell if it's from the pain, as a response to my message to her, or a little bit of both. I squeeze her hand in support.

"I've been to this place dozens, if not hundreds, of times. I know the struggle to endure the pain's iron grasp on your soul. But each time I've made it out of there. So I know that you will too."

I blink back tears, thinking about my own traumatic memories of the merciless pain.

"I *know* your pain will end. You will make it to the other side," I say. "The pain will eventually subside, and it will be such a beautiful, calm moment. Although you are frightened and desperate right now, shaking and frenzied from the pain, you *will* make it out of there. And until you do, I am here with you in this dark hell, sitting next to you. You are not alone."

I can no longer blink back my tears fast enough and they begin to stream down my face. Is she crying down there too?

"Just keep holding on," I encourage her. "You will get through this."

Self-Reflection

Imagine that your friend or loved one is going through a hard time. What can you say to help reassure them that you're there for them and they will get through this?

Take some time to write a caring letter to your friend/loved one: encouraging them, comforting them, and/or reminding them of the qualities that they have that will help them get through this difficult situation. Use second tense language (example: **you** will, **you** are). You don't have to give this letter to them, but you can if you want to!

Now read the letter out loud. Can you soothe yourself in this same loving, caring way when you are having a hard time? The next time you are in a difficult situation, write a caring letter to yourself. If you have trouble writing it, use this letter to your friend as a guide to encourage and comfort yourself.

32

THE MIGHTY OAK INSIDE OF US

It's so rare to have silence. Even when I'm alone, my thoughts, fears, and doubts are still screaming inside my head. I think about one of the Vipassana meditation retreats[1] I went on. The retreat was ten days of silence in which you don't speak or make eye contact with anyone. During that week and a half, you alternate between receiving teachings on the Vipassana meditation technique, meditating, and resting.

"Why are you doing *that?!*" Friends and family had raised their eyebrows in incredulousness when I informed them that I would be out of contact for the ten days of the retreat. They were baffled as to why anyone would want to sit in silence for so long without phones, TV, internet, social interaction, books, friends, or any other form of distraction.

Why? I was curious to see who I really am. What do I have inside, once the voice in my head quiets its comments, anxieties, and incessant judgments? For years, I had no idea that there was anything under that voice. I thought I *was* that voice that rambled on all day, its constant concerns convincing me that it would be pointless—or even dangerous!—to follow my dreams. My inner voice tortured me with my regrets, nagged me about everything it thought I 'should' be doing, and assigned a personal meaning to everything, always assuming the worst case in every scenario. It was never satisfied with the life I have and always wanted more—more money, more happiness, more pain-free days. The decades of misery that annoying voice—a critic, worrier, and pessimist, all rolled into one—had caused me! I wanted it to shut up!

At the retreat, once I was within the quiet meditation halls with nothing to listen to but my mind, the voice in my head amplified at first, bombarding me with memories, plans, and fears. So many fears! As I watched my thoughts go by, it astounded me how they never seemed to stop, and how they could transport me from the past to the future, and to any emotion: the impatience about the clothes I wanted to clean out of the closet once I returned home at the end of the retreat, the realization and subsequent dread that my period would come on a huge work deadline, the regrets I had about how incessantly I complained when I first got sick.

On and on it went, all day long, tens of thousands of thoughts per day—and many of them repetitive—until the fourth day when I noticed that the voice in my head had quieted somewhat. There were still hundreds of thoughts, but there were longer gaps between them where I could simply focus on my breathing without being distracted by my thoughts. Throughout the next six days, I was able to drop progressively deeper into a space of inner quiet and calm.

During the meditation breaks, I would walk the forest path outside. Oak trees towered over me, their green leaves bright against the blue sky. These trees had seen hurricane winds, pounding rain, violent thunderstorms, blazing heat, and freezing cold. In spite of all this, they remained upright; they accepted their fate without worry or fear and were still standing tall.

On the last day of the retreat, I reached my hand out to

touch the bark of one of these majestic reminders of strength. Its uneven ridges felt warm against my hand, and I heard a whisper so quiet that I almost missed it. "You have this same strength," it said.

Was it the voice of the forest? Or had I, after days of solitude, finally found a new inner voice? It was different from the usual voice in my head; it was much gentler and kinder. It didn't matter where it came from, though. It penetrated deep into my soul as a truth I hadn't been able to hear when my mind had been buzzing with nonstop, repetitive, negative chatter.

I, too, have this same profound strength; I, too, have faced countless storms and am still standing. *I am still standing.* Endometriosis, you have not—and will not—beat me. I am stronger than you. I am stronger than your vicious pain.

As I continue to practice Vipassana in my daily life, I'm learning to quiet the screaming and insistent voice of self-sabotage inside my head. I'm pulling out the weeds of worry and replacing them with thought patterns of trust: *The situation will change. Things will work out. They always do.* If anger and frustration try to wrap themselves around my tree's trunk, I cut off those vines with patience and acceptance: *Life is as it is, which will not always be how I want it to be.* When the termites of doubt begin to weaken my tree, I drive them out with confidence: *I can do this. I know I can do this.*

Finding silence within is allowing me to meet my experiences in a different way. It is in that quiet peace that I am learning that I have what I need to get through my pain. *We all do.* We all have this mighty oak of strength, patience, and trust inside of us, waiting to be nurtured. Oftentimes, we just have to cut through the chatter to find it.

Self-Reflection

- What traits do you want to cultivate in yourself? Make a list. Some examples might be: strength, patience, trust, resilience, determination.
- Now go down the list, focusing on each trait one at a time. Do you have any of that trait already?
- Recall a time when having that trait helped you, or would have helped you. What were the circumstances?
- If you had more of this trait, what benefit would it bring you? For example, could it help you cope, or worry less, or get through the day?
- What can you do to cultivate this trait in yourself?
- When you consider cultivating this trait, what obstacles show up? For example, you want to work on your confidence but are full of doubt. Can you use this 'obstacle' as a reminder to strengthen the trait you want to grow?

33

A LIFEBOAT IN A STORM OF EMOTIONS

I sit often with my illness to see what comes up. What does it mean to 'sit with' something? It means to stay present with it, to 'be with' it without distracting myself to escape it, and to notice what sensations I feel in my body.

I notice the lump in my throat from sadness when I think about how many opportunities I've missed out on because of severe fatigue.

I notice the burning in my face from shame when I think about some of the flares that left me collapsing in pain in front of coworkers or strangers.

I notice the jittery feeling of panic when I think about the eternity of the word *incurable.*

I notice the tension in my muscles from fear as I think about my period approaching.

I notice the hollow emptiness of loneliness, as I think about how my loved ones don't understand the depth of my pain.

It's been strange to intentionally let in emotions that I have been pushing away most of my life. Many of them are uncomfortable; some of them outright terrify me. For most of my life, my relationship with my emotions has been to run away from them or to repress them. When an uncomfortable feeling used to rise in my body, my first subconscious inclination was to distract myself from it—scrolling through social media feeds, watching movies, or tackling my to-do list. When I was busy, I could ignore my feelings. Sometimes, they were too overwhelming to avoid, and in those cases I would comfort myself through eating or shopping, in an attempt to run *toward* the emotion of happiness.

But now I'm doing something different. I'm sitting with and observing my emotions, trying to really look at them and stop running from them.[1] In doing so, I can see that just like with my thoughts, my emotions are passing and impermanent. When sadness arrives, it's heavy and stagnates me; I want to lie down and stop moving. When joy is present, it's light and airy; I want to jump and skip. When anger visits, it's a heat that wants to explode out of me; I want to break things or scream in frustration. Sometimes, these emotions are intense, but always, these emotions pass.

Subconsciously, I used to worry that if I felt my emotions in all of their rawness that they might break me apart. Ironically, though, what seemed to be destroying me was not the feelings themselves but trying to ignore them when they were screaming to be heard. The more I avoided and suppressed them, the more they festered. The more I pushed them away and rejected them, the more I pushed away and rejected a part of myself.

I've recently realized that if I want to be whole, I can no longer ignore my emotions or pick and choose between them. Like it or not, anger, sadness, and fear are just as much a part of me as joy is. I have to acknowledge them and even invite them in. The parts of me that want to lie down and stop moving, or break things and scream—they aren't pathetic or a sign that I'm failing at life, as I once thought they were. These emotions are human. And they are part of *all* of us.

I feel ready to get to know my full self. I'm still scared and uncomfortable, but my tolerance to sit with my feelings has been growing. When a strong emotion arises, I name it: "Disappointment," I say as I recognize the pulling sensation in my chest; "Frustration," I say as the heat starts to bubble up. Identifying the feelings shifts me into a state of awareness. When I didn't know what I was feeling—when it was just an overwhelming, jumbled mess of unwanted, uncomfortable, distressing energy I was trying to avoid—I didn't know what that feeling was communicating to me or what I needed. Now, I can see that emotions visit in response to something that's happened: sadness might be asking me to cry (which can help relieve stress by excreting stress hormones through tears) or to let go of an attachment to something. Anger may be signaling to me that my boundaries have been crossed, or even give me the energy and push to take action in response to injustice.

I'm giving my emotions permission to be there. We are part of a society that demonizes most of our emotions—after years of hearing messages like: "Calm down!"; "You shouldn't get so upset over this;" "Don't cry;" and "It's not 'ladylike' to be so angry," I had internalized the idea that it wasn't acceptable to feel anything but happiness.

The challenge isn't just to sit with my emotions but to sit without judging myself for having them. It's not helpful to tell myself that I deserve to feel embarrassed, upset, or sad, or that what I'm feeling is wrong. Sometimes, as I sit with a difficult feeling, I put my hand on my heart, close my eyes, and tell myself these simple yet powerful words: "It's okay to feel this way." Self-compassion is a much needed lifeboat in the storm of feelings that's life.

Like all storms, the emotions eventually pass. In the same way that a physical itch or pain are impermanent, my emotions are too. The more I practice sitting with my emotions, the easier it's becoming to be with them. Many people have written about the freedom they've found by learning to embrace what they feel. They aren't controlled by their anger, frozen into inaction by fear, or disappointed with themselves for having sad days. I, too, want to find that freedom and live from it.

Self-Reflection

- Do you ever repress or avoid your emotions instead of allowing yourself to feel them? How often?
- Why? Take a moment to write down a time you've repressed or avoided emotions and why you did so. For example, you don't like feeling angry; you were too busy to let joy overwhelm you; you believe that to be strong, you can't show fear; you believe there's no need to feel sadness.
- Do you think it's helpful to repress or avoid your emotions? Take a few minutes and think about this. There's no wrong or right answer; the goal is to understand yourself.
- Do you think there are any consequences on your mental or emotional health when people repress or avoid their emotions?
- When you have a feeling that is often considered 'negative' by society, such as sadness, anger, or frustration, how do you work through it?
- Do you have any unhealthy coping mechanisms to avoid or soothe your feelings, running toward escape and happiness? For example, comfort eating, drinking, smoking, binge watching series, or staying constantly busy?
- If you find yourself repressing or avoiding your emotions over the next week, take a second to acknowledge that emotion and analyze it, no matter

how small it seems. For example, "I'm feeling disappointed because I was hoping to go for a walk but it's raining."

Make sure to reach out to a qualified mental health professional or a loved one should you need support in sitting with or acknowledging emotions.

34

A NARROWING WORLD

A memory from college.

As pain and fatigue limit my mobility, my world is shrinking. I can barely leave my bed, let alone expend the energy needed to go shopping, drive thirty minutes to the beach, or walk across campus to class. I can't even enjoy reading or crosswords in bed because the brain fog is so thick. Although a few friends said they don't mind just hanging out in my dorm room, I can't find it in me to invite them over. Making conversation with my happy, carefree friends about the dates they've gone on or what field we want to major in just deepens my feelings of isolation and loneliness. Those used to be the topics on my mind, but they aren't anymore—I now worry about how much money all the medical bills are adding up to and when (if ever) I will feel better. I don't know anyone else who is sick, and I feel completely alone.

Not to mention, I don't want my friends to see me in this state: curled up in bed, running off mid-sentence to the toilet, eyes closing from fatigue while I speak. It's embarrassing, and my self-confidence has been shaken to the core. Something heavy weighs down on me—perhaps it's a feeling of vulnerability?—as everything I love and have taken for granted is being snatched away from me by this disease.

As my world gets smaller, I'm losing more than just the activities and friends I used to have—I'm losing a sense of belonging. I never realized how deeply we as humans crave connection to the people and world around us. I've been fired from my job for repeated absences; I've stopped hanging out with my friends and may even need to take a medical leave from college. My place in this world has been swallowed up by pain and nausea. I don't fit into my life anymore, and that fills me with anguish and loss.

Self-Reflection

- Do you feel like your world closed in on you since you first fell ill?
- Have you lost your sense of connection or belonging?
- Do you ever feel isolated, lonely, or like no one understands what you are going through?
- How do you cope with these feelings?
- Do you have someone you can reach out to when you feel like this? For example, a friend, a loved one, a mental health professional?
- Are there any ways that you could find more connection and belonging in your life? For example, could you join a support group, connect with others in the endometriosis community via social media, or volunteer?

35

THE LIGHT IN MY HEART

What would it be like to be a star in the sky? Would I feel lonely as I look out onto the vastness of the universe? Or would I feel the depth of the incredible power and mystery that the universe holds?

Were I a star, majestic light would shine out from my heart with radiance and glory, filling every crevice of the universe with its brilliance and splendor. It would take away the darkness, it would warm hearts that had turned bitter and cold, and it would guide those who are lost.

Daydreaming of being a star reminds me of a fact that I forgot: I am so much more than my body, my endometriosis, and my daily burdens. While I am not a star, a beautiful light already does live inside my heart—in the form of love.

When did I forget that I am full of love? When did loneliness start to disconnect me from my heart? When did I lose my sense of being part of something greater than myself?

Was it when the pain began? Pain can be so lonely. Even when someone I love is right there with me, rubbing my back as it breaks in half or holding my hair as I throw up, that cold, dark world of pain in my body is mine and mine alone. Oftentimes, I feel isolated from my loved ones while I live in a world where they don't understand the depth of my pain. Nor do *I* understand why I have so much pain. While I have a rudimentary scientific understanding of how the physical mechanisms of endometriosis can cause me pain (tissue in my body that shouldn't be there, secreting inflammatory chemicals and irritating the surrounding tissue; organs fusing together from adhesions; pelvic floor dysfunction; etc), what baffles me is why pain has to exist in this universe at all.

It is one of the great mysteries that I will never have the answer to. Sometimes, I conclude that the purpose of pain is to remind me to cherish the times without it. Other times, it helps me to think that pain exists to present me with challenges to help me strengthen my spirit and grow. But these are just conjectures, meanings that I've attached to it. There are many times, too, when pain just feels like pointless suffering.

But when I'm in pain, even though I often feel emotionally isolated from loved ones, the experience *is* always just a little less heavy when someone is there with me to hold my hand. Even on the many occasions when I've been physically alone, hugging my *Get well soon* dolly has given me some comfort. It makes me think that maybe the question is not why pain exists but rather why *love* exists. Maybe love exists to open our hearts and get us through the hard times. Maybe it's to connect us and push us to be there for each other.

I've been reflecting recently on what love means to me. Is it simply an emotion? Not to me—love is my underlying nature, a state of being, an energy within me, a powerful force that is present even though I forget at times, even when I'm trapped in fear, even if it doesn't seem available to me. Love is always there, waiting to be found. To me, forgiveness is a form of love. Acceptance is a form of love. Surrender and trust are forms of love. As I work on opening my heart to endometriosis, I'm trying to invite the many forms of love to carry me through this journey.

Self-Reflection

- Why do you think love (not romantic love, but a more abstract idea of love) exists in this world?
- What do you think love is? Is it an emotion, or it is something deeper than that, like a state of being, an energy, or a light?
- Do you feel that love also comes in the form of acceptance, or trust, or a state of mind?
- Has the energy of love helped you through any of your hard times?

36

APPRECIATING THE PAIN-FREE MOMENTS

I remember one day when I was living in the rainforest, walking from my hut to a large communal garden. Like most days, the sun was beating down relentlessly. Paths through the trees in the rainforest are lush, green, and alive, but the clearings, like the one I was walking through at the time, are extremely dry from the heat of the sun. My throat felt as parched as the dusty ground below. The dirt was hardened and cracked; I could see the heat sizzling on the surface. The village was still, lifeless under the punishing sun. The only movement and sound was that of a chicken clucking lazily at me as I walked by.

My feet crunched along on the dry earth as I started to walk faster. The sun was so hot; how it burned on my face! There was an old, abandoned hut on the edge of the open plaza, and I stepped under it. Oh, sweet, sweet shade! The roof kept the hut slightly darker and cooler, and I breathed a sigh of relief to have to sun off my face.

Looking back now, it makes me wonder. If the entire path was shaded and I never had to step into the sun, would I feel as grateful for the constant shade? Or would I just take it for granted, complaining about the heat, never knowing it could be worse?

Knowing myself, I would probably just take it for granted. After all, that's what I did with each pain-free moment I've had over the last decade. Those moments were like those little pockets of shade along that village path, but I failed to appreciate them. I'd been holding on so tightly to wanting to be 100% better that I completely overlooked the fact that I *did* have little moments of relief.

My attitude has been changing though. I've been dwelling much less on how awful the bad moments are and instead letting their existence serve as a wakeup call to really value the good ones. In comparison to the unbearable moments of pain, the regular humdrum—but pain-free!—moments of my life, like doing household chores, starting a work project, or cooking my dinner, are blissful and beautiful.

I often recall my days in the rainforest. It was so easy there to have gratitude for the blissful moments, be it swimming in the river to cool off from the midday heat or when the clouds would roll in and rain would fall from the sky, replenishing the buckets that collected our drinking water. There was the sweetness of the fresh papayas that we picked off the trees, the golden sunlight during the first hours of dawn, the double rainbows in the sky after the rainfall, the excitement of catching a fish in the river, and the kindness of the community that I was living with.

There were many miserable moments as well. There was the scorching heat that burned my skin; the tarantulas, ants, and cockroaches in every corner of the cabin; the relentless itching as the mosquitos and sandflies devoured me; the slippery mud after the rainfall that I always fell down in; the heavy humidity that made fungus grow everywhere, from my clothes to my skin.

I laughed with the villagers, I screamed from the terror of

finding myself face-to-face (on multiple occasions) with a tarantula, I relaxed in a plastic chair (there were very few actual chairs as we mostly sat on benches or logs) on the porch reading an enthralling novel, I dripped with sweat in the stifling heat. I took the bad with the good because it was a beautiful, unique experience and I knew that once it ended, I would never get to relive any of it.

Shouldn't I feel this way about my life? When it's over, there will be no going back. When a pain-free moment turns into a painful moment, I can't go back and relive the pain-free moment once I belatedly realize how great it actually was. By that time, it's gone. I remember not too long ago holding that squished lilac in my hand, a symbol to me of the fragility of life. Although I don't like to admit it, at any minute I could die, from an accident or for any other reason. But if I can let that understanding guide me in the present instead of panicking and scaring me, then I can realize what's before me—a life with a full range of experiences. There are symptom-filled days, but those can wake me up to the precious days, hours, or even simply minutes that I am symptom-free.

Self-Reflection

- Think of a time when being sick temporarily deprived you of something (big or small). For example, a time you had to call out of work, or a time when you couldn't get out of bed for three days, or after surgery when you couldn't put on your shoes without assistance. How did it feel not being able to do this or to have those limitations?
- Now, recall when you were able to do that activity again. What feelings did you have when that limitation was gone? Did you have a feeling of

gratitude for being able to do the activity again or simply frustration that it was ever taken from you?
- Did having that limitation make you realize that you previously took that activity for granted?
- Did any feelings of appreciation fade as time went by and you regularly did that activity?
- Next, think of something (for example, an ability, item, a person's friendship) you currently take for granted. Write about what it would be like to *not* have this. In what ways would that lack complicate or change your life? Would it cause you stress or hardship?
- Now, come back to the present moment and acknowledge that you do have this thing. Do you feel more grateful for it after having imagined yourself without it?

Every night, practice consciously appreciating one thing from your day, no matter how small, such as the ability to put on your shoes on your own, the deliciousness of the food you had for dinner, or the presence of another person in your life. If you are stuck and can't think of anything at all, you can use this activity of imagining the difficulties of your life *without* a certain thing to appreciate your current life *with* it.

37

THE VALUE OF MY LOVING PRESENCE

Who would I be if I stripped away all of the negative labels that I've put on myself, labels like *stupid, worthless, useless, unproductive, ugly,* and *burdensome?* Who would I be if I decided that I *wasn't* broken? If I decided that there was nothing inherently wrong with me? If I stopped thinking that I was inadequate? Or a bad person? What would shine through if I didn't believe these stories about myself?

The idea of *not being enough* and *inadequacy* is pushed on us from when we are young. How many of us are plagued by the notion that we aren't productive enough? Or smart enough? Or beautiful enough? We may not say to ourselves, "I don't think I'm X enough," but our self-talk or self-sabotaging behavior reveals to us that this belief is behind the scenes, impacting our thoughts, decisions, and emotions every day of our lives. It's easy to absorb negative messaging about ourselves it's when all around us: when we are being told by societal norms, by advertising, by bullies, by loved ones, by teachers, by TV, and so many other influences that we should be one way or another, and if we aren't, then we don't measure up. Models in magazines are photoshopped to look more like society's idea of 'beautiful';

tabloids love to gossip about celebrities with they run errands without makeup or in sweatpants—as if there's something wrong with not being glamorous all the time; there's a constant pressure to ace the next test, to work longer hours, to fit in, to adjust every piece of you to cater to those around you. Yet these imposed expectations of beauty, intelligence, and productivity—to name a few—are often unrealistic, unachievable, or unsustainable.

I want to break this conditioning and stop telling myself how stupid, worthless, and ugly I am. I want to have a new pattern of thinking about myself, one that highlights my value instead of cuts me down. But how do I actually find my value when it's been hidden by all the lies I've been told?

I look over at my dolly who is lying on the bed, her fuchsia hair standing straight up in typical troll doll fashion. She is an inanimate object, yet she has helped me get through some of the worst moments of my life. She has always been there for me. I don't know how I would have endured such indescribable pain if I hadn't had her to hug in the middle of the night, if I hadn't had the comfort and love she gave me with her presence, if I hadn't had her listening ear to open up to. On more than one occasion, she has saved me from my loneliness; I've broken down sobbing with gratitude that she was there with me, thanking her for not leaving me alone with my pain in my otherwise empty apartment. Although she is just an inanimate doll, her comforting presence is enough to make her extremely important to me.

What about my partner? He sits with me when I'm in pain and gently holds my hand. He doesn't mind when I cancel our dinner plans due to a flare; he's happy to instead stay in and watch a movie together.

What about my friend? She listens when I'm having a rough day and validates my experiences. Her sharp sense of humor helps me laugh instead of cry when dealing with my symptoms.

Nothing that I named about them or my dolly has to do with being perfect, gorgeous, or productive. Their value is in their loving presence—just as it is with *me*. If I took away all of the layers of who I am, or rather who I believe myself to be, I would see that is also where my value lies: in my hugs, my listening ear, my ability to share a laugh, the company I provide, the interest I take in others around me, the comfort I give them when they have a bad day. It doesn't matter if I'm beautiful, work extra hours, get straight As, or don't quite fit in—I have value. I matter. We *all* do.

While my feelings of inadequacy are deep-rooted and difficult to break, I'm starting to see a bigger picture of myself. I am full of love that I give freely and openly to those around me, and that is just one positive trait I have of what I'm sure are many. One of the skills I'm gaining on this journey with endometriosis is how to also give that love freely and openly to myself.

Self-Reflection

- Think of a loved one and describe at least five of their best characteristics. What do you love about them? Try to go for the deeper essence. For example, if you write, *I love my friend because she always checks in with me after I have a doctor's appointment,* then the essence under that might actually be, *I love my friend because she is thoughtful.* Look over your list. Do you think they know they have these wonderful qualities?
- Now, take a loving, open-minded look at yourself. Why do you think that your loved ones love you? Write at least five of your characteristics as if you were looking at yourself through an outside lens. For example, *Amy always does the dishes after dinner because she's considerate.*

- Once you've finished your list, take a minute to look it over and really value these qualities about yourself.
- Where do you feel you are 'inadequate' or 'not enough' in your life?
- Take a few minutes to think about where those thoughts came from, and look again at your list to see how you do have value and positive qualities.
- How could your positive qualities shine even further if you had fewer of these feelings of inadequacy toward yourself?
- Would anything change in your relationships with loved ones? Would you be a better listener, more playful, able to laugh more, happier?

38

THE UNSHAKEABLE TRUST I HAVE IN THE SUN

The sun always rises. No matter the weather, no matter the day, no matter the circumstances, the sun follows its path through the sky, calm and determined. Have I ever woken up worried that the sun wouldn't rise? No, that would be silly—the sun always rises. Just like the clouds always cross the sky. Just like *I* always make it to the other side of my pain, my concerns, and my worries.

Sitting outside in the peacefulness of this perfect summer day, I realize one of the reasons why I'm suffering so deeply: I don't fully believe in my ability to get through my health problems. I doubt myself; I'm filled with uncertainty. Who could blame me? Endometriosis is unpredictable. I have sudden flares, and symptoms change from one day to the next. What if a flare comes while I'm at the grocery store? What if I'm in too much pain to sleep so the next day, from pure exhaustion, I have to call out of work?

Yet, every day I rise to my challenges, just as every day the sun rises in the sky. In situation after situation, I have put one foot in front of the other, no matter the circumstances in my life. I have shown myself to be resilient in spite of the worst. I need to start having the same unwavering faith in my ability to get through my problems as I do in the sun coming up tomorrow, the next day, and the day after that. How can I cultivate in myself that same unshakeable trust that I have in the sun?

Like in so many other aspects of my life, my thoughts are crucial. My toxic habit of continually doubting myself erodes my self-confidence. If trust is the foundation on which I want to build my life, self-judgment is a hammer chipping away at it, brick by brick, crumbling the foundation's ability to be sturdy and hold weight. Self-compassion, however, is the mortar that holds the bricks steady in place.

First, I need to learn why I constantly feel that I'm letting myself down—which makes me constantly doubt my decisions and worry that the future will go poorly for me. My negative self-assessment comes from a subconscious belief that I should be doing everything perfectly. With that lens, I look at my past and am filled with regrets:

I should have researched more into the side effects of that hormone shot, and then I never would have taken it and suffered so deeply with the relentless side effects it caused.

I shouldn't have stopped advocating for myself, and then I might have gotten diagnosed sooner.

I should have made dietary changes as soon as I got sick, and then I might not have had chronic diarrhea during college.

I should have found more ways to empower myself early on instead of sitting around crying and complaining.

Notice the word 'should' starts every regret: *I should have done this, I shouldn't have done that, I should have, I should have.*

I should have, but I didn't. I can't change that, and now I don't trust myself in the present day because I feel like in the past I let myself down over and over again. I love to keep kicking myself for 'screwing up', but how easy is it today to look back on my decisions of five or ten years with hindsight? That's not fair to myself. I didn't have the information or experience that I do now! I also forget how exhausted I was in some of those moments, how overwhelmed I was, how scared I was, how confused I was, how much pain I was in—how much I was suffering.

Of course, I can relive the past and make different choices in my mind, but what's the point? It's just an empty fantasy that tortures me and further contributes to my unhappiness with the way I actually acted. The past is done and over with; the things that happened cannot be changed.

Does it matter anyway what I 'should' have done? What matters is where I'm at now:

I did eventually get diagnosed—not as quickly as I would have liked, but the fact that I got my diagnosis means I have tenacity and persistence!

I may not have changed right away to a more-fitting lifestyle that helped improve my quality of life, but ever since I did more than a decade ago, I've been fully committed to it!

I didn't know to research about the hormone shot, but that awful experience with its side effects drilled into me that I must always do so before making any treatment decisions. That lesson has been invaluable to helping me eventually find excision surgery among the relentless misinformation that plagues endometriosis.

I have not always done everything right, but no one has, and no one will. Can I let go of perfection? Instead, can I embrace the wisdom that my messy life experience has brought me? Every 'mistake' I've made has driven me forward; I have been changing and growing over the years. I may not have gotten through my challenges with the grace that I would have liked, but I still got through every single one of them!

Throughout all of it, I have never given up on myself. That is what I need to hold onto when life goes dark and moving forward seems impossible: the knowledge that the sun has always always risen, even after the blackest night; the knowledge that I have always gotten through the most unbearable situations—even when I thought I wouldn't. Even when I was wracked with anxiety and fear, even when I was completely overwhelmed, even when I thought the situation was hopeless and I was filled with despair, *I made it through.*

In fortifying my trust in myself—and hence the confidence I have in my ability to get through anything—my mind has less worry and stress, and more equanimity.

> Equanimity: meaning to be calm and composed, to have a balanced mind, to be undisturbed by the external chaos around me.

That sounds so beautiful to me—to maintain internal peace and serenity although everything external is falling apart, something that I find happens frequently when living with a devastating illness like endometriosis.

I hadn't realized how blocked my heart has been by self-doubt, regret, and worry. It's been like a poison, seeping into every aspect of my life, affecting not only how I see myself, but also my moods, my social relationships, and the decisions I've made. The more I learn to trust in myself, the better my relationship with this uncertain and unpredictable life gets. I can see that learning to love and accept myself fully—as an imperfect human being that is bound to make mistakes—is one of the most vital acts of healing I can give myself.

Self-Reflection

- Think of a time that you feel you let yourself down. Looking back without judgment, why do you feel that you disappointed yourself?
- Does feeling that you've disappointed yourself help

improve your current situation, mindset, or self-confidence?

- What do you wish you had done differently in that situation?
- Explore with curiosity—but not judgment—why you didn't do that in the first place. Were you missing something that you have now, like experience, knowledge, confidence, or a support system?
- Can you look back on that situation with compassion toward yourself and see that you did the best that you could?
- Now, think of a time when you were worried about something but you came through for yourself. How did you show up for yourself? For example, maybe you were worried about an exam you had to take, buying a new car in your price range, or taking care of a sick child. Did you study for the exam, spend hours researching about cars, or bring your child to the doctor?
- How did you take action to help yourself through the situation?
- Do you trust yourself to get through difficult times and situations? Or do you have a lot of self-doubt?
- If you tend to have self-doubt, think more about times you've come through for yourself. Can you try to start working on your self-confidence and self-trust and help your worrying go down?

39

INTEGRATING ILLNESS INTO MY LIFE

Endometriosis is forever. It's never, ever going away. Is it possible to accept something ongoing that won't ever be a closed chapter of my life?

I once agonized over this question, but every day I'm accepting circumstances that I thought I would never in a million years be able to accept.

It helps that I am more adjusted to my new life of pain and fatigue. For years, I've been figuring out how to integrate chronic illness into my everyday life. I suppose that has been an unexpected silver lining of having endometriosis symptoms completely shatter my daily routines and identity. As I go through the emotionally wrenching task of rebuilding my life to accommodate endometriosis, I'm making space for this disease and focusing on the idea of trying to live well with it.

This has meant figuring out new hobbies to enjoy that I am actually able to participate in—even with limited mobility or energy. It has meant changing careers from teaching to an office job so that I can have more flexibility in my schedule and not have to expend as much energy as I did in the classroom. It has meant getting out into nature as often as possible to remind myself that I am part of a much bigger world than the bubble of illness I can feel trapped in. I'm redefining my self-worth, my priorities, and even what intimacy means. I'm trying to stop dwelling on what I *used* to be able to do and instead focus on what I can do *now*. I'm finding new ways to have meaning and feel fulfilled. I've found a community of online friends who understand what it's like to have chronic illness, and we mutually support each other on the worst days. All of these ways of integrating endometriosis into my life is contributing to a newfound sense of belonging and connection to the world—which is reducing my feelings of inadequacy, self-hatred, and loneliness.

I'm using questions to empower myself and explore ways to better my life: What can I do to get through the difficult moments when I'm in too much pain to even cry? What lifestyle modifications can I make to improve my symptoms, even incrementally? How do I want to feel about the changes endometriosis has brought to my life?

The last question is really the driving force. I want to feel at peace, and the internal practices I've been developing over the past few years are helping me get there as they grow my capacity to deal with this devastating disease. Meditation, cognitive reframing, gratitude, forgiveness, cultivating meaning, working through emotions via journaling—these are all turning me inwards, teaching me how to cope with the pain and balance out the negative.

My original goal for these practices was to change from hating endometriosis to being neutral toward it. I wanted to open myself more so that I could better tolerate my circumstances and not be so bitter and afraid. But now I can see that these practices are taking me even further—they are showing me how to participate in my life instead of just letting it happen to me. They are showing me that I can meet my experiences with a boundless and expansive heart: with joy, with love, with trust in myself.

For so long, I thought that I wasn't making any progress with acceptance, but as time passes, I look back and see that I am moving forward. The movement is imperceptible in the moment it happens; it's a 0.1% increase from the day before that I don't even notice. But little by little, it's adding up. Each small insight is helping me gain more control over how I feel and take back my life from endometriosis.

Self-Reflection

Answer these questions for yourself (feel free to replace *endometriosis* with something else you're working through):

- What can I do to live with endometriosis?
- What can I do to get through the difficult moments?
- What lifestyle modifications can I make to improve my symptoms?
- How do I want to feel about the changes endometriosis has brought to my life?

40

SURRENDERING TO THE PAIN

Note: This essay contains descriptions of pain that some readers may find upsetting.

The room narrows and goes dark; there is only extreme pain and survival. It's a waiting game. *Please, let me get through this.*

I know that I should focus on my breath. Breathe slowly and deeply—but where is my breath? This pain is choking me; I gasp and pant shallowly. Consumed by pain, I cease to be me. I'm no longer Amy the daughter, Amy the teacher, Amy the joyful woman who loves making art. I'm not anything that makes me who I am. I'm only pain. It defines me, controls me, makes my soul feel so lost that I no longer care if I were to die in this moment. I would do anything to end this torture that permeates my mind and my spirit.

I find a brief moment of control. "Shhh," I soothe myself, "You're okay, you're okay." I repeat this over and over to myself, frenzied from the pain, "You're okay, you're okay."

I stumble to the toilet where the neighbors probably hear my screams as I poop out knives and simultaneously vomit into the garbage can. Snot and puke splatter my face. I hunch over on the toilet, rocking and sobbing. The pain is too much. I shake and shiver; I start to hyperventilate. I feel the blood drain out of my arms and legs and myself going white. "Breathe deeper," I tell myself. "You're about to faint."

Minutes drag slowly into hours. Time is warped when I am in such pain. Minutes are no longer measured in seconds but only in waves of pain, gasps of breath, trips to the toilet. I change positions every few seconds, but it doesn't matter if I'm lying down, pacing, curled up in a ball, or bent at the waist clutching my back—the pain remains absolutely unbearable. Time stretches before me, pain stretches before me, and I start to find myself delusional, wondering if the pain will actually end, second-guessing if I am in this level of extreme pain because I might be dying. Pain is an alarm signal in the body, and my brain is starting to panic. Am I dying? I don't know. I'm just on the toilet, puking, sobbing silently.

My only job right now is to survive. Time does not exist. Counting the minutes only makes them drag on longer. *This is just a moment,* I remind myself, *on top of a moment, on top of another moment. I can get through a moment.*

Eighteen thousand moments later, comprising some five hours, a miracle happens. There is nothing in my life that makes me more grateful than when that brutal pain subsides just a small bit. I can feel how my body stops spasming as the pain drops down a notch. The relief! It feels like the dust settling after an old building is knocked down. It's dirty, chaotic, and a reminder of the destruction that just was, but at the same time it's beautiful because once the rubble is cleaned up, the hope is to build something new.

And now, the aftermath. Trying to find the little pieces of my soul that blew apart when the wrecking ball hit my uterus. This is probably the second hardest part of my period. Trying to make sense of it all, trying to move past it. Forcing myself to remember that it's not my fault, that life isn't fair, and I shouldn't expect it to be.

For the next one or two days, the pain is still excruciating. It's impossible to move without crying out, but while excruciating, it's still a step down from what it was. At least I'm no longer writhing in agony, and I can be aware of other sensations now that the pain has stopped consuming me. I can feel the softness of the sheets and the cool breeze of the fan against my forehead. I can finally focus on my breath flowing in and out of me. I put my hand on my chest and feel it rising and falling. I'm here, I'm alive; I made it through another month. I look around my bedroom with its inspirational quotes on the walls, and for the first time in hours, I feel safe again in my own body.

Mindfulness: I have started practicing it during my period in an attempt to change my relationship with pain. It has not been easy. At first, trying to bring awareness to such a horrible experience felt like I was sadistically trying to torture myself. But surprisingly, it's actually been extremely helpful to disentangle myself from all the emotional suffering I create around the physical pain.

I can't take painkillers anymore, and trying to skip my periods through hormone therapy came with miserable daily side effects. I have been trying alternative therapies, but nothing so far has alleviated the pain. For now, I am stuck with my period, stuck with the endless hours of backbreaking torment that always comes with it. What else can I do but learn to be with it and learn how to wait for it to pass?

What actually *is* being mindful? How can I 'be with' pain? It's being present to the moment that I am in: a moment of pain. It's doable to survive a moment, but the same cannot be said about hours and hours. Being with pain means no more panicking about how many grueling hours I have left; no more begging out loud in desperation for it to stop. No more wishing the pain away. None of that actually makes the pain go away—it just makes me feel hopeless and in despair. Inevitably and eventually, this pain that makes me go out of my skin will end in its own time. Just as it arose in my body, it will dissipate. Just like everything in life, the pain is impermanent. Although my pain is chronic and with me every day, these spikes of *severe* pain do come and go. The less I resist the pain, the easier it is to just wait for it to pass.

Mindfulness means reframing the experience of pain in my mind without *judging* it like we so naturally do—without assigning any feelings to it and instead just letting it exist. Judging the pain is natural. But in reality? Having hours of excruciating pain is not 'an awful experience' as I often say, nor 'a sad experience.' *Of course it's bad,* my mind argues. *Look what it does to you!* And my mind is right, in a way—what it does to me feels terrible. But really, at its core, the pain is neither a good or bad experience—it's just an experience. If I really want to put a descriptive word to it, perhaps I can call my pain 'a human experience' because there is no life without pain. In fact, it's not *my* pain, per say. It's just pain—the pain of being human, the pain of life, the pain of endometriosis. But it's not 'mine'. It just exists. And as much as I don't want to have an experience like excruciating pain, adding my judgment to it, adding my hatred to it, doesn't change the fact that the pain exists.

When I view an experience as bad, I tend to despise it. I've lived in hatred for years: hating my body, hating the pain, hating what endometriosis puts me through, hating myself. The list didn't end there. I used to hate so many things—long airplane rides, Mondays at work, going to the grocery store. But what did all that hatred accomplish—all that judgment of those experiences? Hating something filled me with dread *prior* to having the actual experience; it also filled me with misery while it was happening. When I flew, I was miserable on the plane, counting the hours until I'd be free from my torture; I was miserable *before and after* my flight, as I dreaded it, tried to avoid it, complained about it, and continued feeling angry about it once the experience ended. What did judging having the flight accomplish? Only lengthening my misery. A three hour flight turned into an entire day of unhappiness.

That is why I'm now surrendering to the things I used to loathe, such as my pain. I can't change my pain. I've certainly tried every medicine, herbal supplement, vitamin, dietary change, and exercise routine I have come across. But my pain is still with me. I have to have that experience, just like I have to get on a ten hour flight every time I want to return to the US from Japan to visit my family.

What does it mean to surrender? To stop resisting it, to stop trying to control it, to let it in, to shrug my shoulders and say, "Oh well." Since I started simply accepting experiences in my life, the things I used to hate no longer seem like such a big deal. They are losing their power over me, and I see this sentiment echoed in different aspects of my life: the more nonjudgmental I am, the freer I become.

Endometriosis is endometriosis. That's it. It's not 'good', not 'bad'. I need to stop putting it into these dualistic categories. It just exists in my life; it's something neutral, just as the toaster is neutral to me, and the pillows on my bed, and the clouds in the sky. I feel nothing toward the toaster, the pillows, or the clouds, and that's how I want to feel toward endometriosis.

Don't get me wrong—mindfulness doesn't make the physical pain hurt any less. I am still vomiting and having diarrhea uncontrollably; I'm still thrashing about on the floor, with no position able to alleviate the crushing sensation in my back. But psychologically, the pain has become less overwhelming and less distressing than it was. Mindfulness helps with the emotional dimension of the pain—with the stories I build around it and myself, and the second arrow of judgment and criticism that I quickly shoot myself with. Mindfulness has helped me become more confident in my ability to handle the unbearable pain, and I have stopped panicking about whether it will eventually end—because it certainly will.

The worst of the pain will fade just like it arose. Like the tide on the shore must recede, like the sun in the sky must set, like our breath must exhale and our chest must fall. Endometriosis pain is a storm that surges up from the sea when conditions are right, and it will dissipate just as quickly after it has run its course. When it's the right time, it will be over, but no one knows when that will be. And that's okay—however long it is, I will make it through, moment by moment.

Self-Reflection

- How does time feel to you when you are in pain (especially severe pain)? Does it drag on endlessly, or does it disappear? How does a few minutes in pain feel to you? Does it feel like a few minutes or like hours?
- When you are in pain, do you ever experience feelings of panic or fear that the pain will never end?
- Do you ever begin to count the minutes or lament how long you have been in pain?
- Does focusing on the time diminish the pain or intensify it?
- Do you judge your pain as good or bad?
- What is your relationship with your pain? Do you dread, fear, or hate it?
- Do you think it's possible to change your relationship with your pain?
- What kind of relationship would you like to have with it?
- What is a way you can make a step in that direction?

41

THE COMPLICATED RULES OF ENDOMETRIOSIS

A creative writing piece on the pressure I feel to take care of myself to avoid flares.

Sometimes, I feel like I'm caught in a synchronized dance with endometriosis, a dance that my well-being depends upon. I was thrown onto the dance floor at seventeen years old without a clue about the moves. For the past sixteen years, I've been learning the complicated steps of this dance. There are thousands of them, and I've fallen down, gotten hurt, and even lost hope at times. I've mentally exhausted myself trying to learn the steps: adequate sleep, daily movement, special diet, lifestyle changes, repeat.

When I excel at this dance, it's breathtaking in its beauty and grace. It often keeps me from having flares; it often keeps the daily fatigue and pain at bay. When I see these positive benefits, the dance is worth the hassle. On a few occasions, I've even found myself reflecting that this tedious dance with endometriosis has been a blessing in disguise, motivating me to really take excellent care of myself.

After all, for the first two years of this illness, I was barely able to function. Then, I serendipitously found the book on managing Epstein-Barr symptoms in the secondhand store, opening my eyes to the role I play in my health through diet and lifestyle—that's when I took my first steps onto this dance floor. I stuck with it, despite how many times I stumbled, and now I am able to get out of bed, get off the toilet, and even hold a steady job!

But of course, just when I start dancing effortlessly, the music changes. New symptoms and new flare triggers will appear suddenly, and I'll find myself in a new song with unfamiliar steps—just as detailed and challenging, but drastically different than what I'm used to. Suddenly, I'm left scrambling to learn the intricacies of the new dance. Once again, all the steps are a curse. One little mistake, and my health crumbles around me.

It's empowering that I can influence how I feel. It's also exhausting. I dance frantically, all day, every day, but I take just one 'wrong' step and BAM!—debilitating pain. It feels like my entire world is focused on preventing pain. That's a lot of responsibility to have had every day since I was seventeen years old. I've now been doing this for sixteen years, and I probably have another fifty to go. I don't want to dance chronically, every second of my life. I feel like I am stuck on the dance floor, unable to escape, dancing forever with endometriosis.

What if I try to leave the dance floor? What if I simply quit this dance? But how can I, knowing that every health decision can make or break how I feel? Of course, there is a difference between taking responsibility for how I feel and blaming myself. My problem is that this line is blurred for me, and I often find myself dancing into the territory of self-blame, guilt, and shame without even realizing it. When I skip exercising and then my legs hurt, I blame myself: "If I had taken my daily walk, this wouldn't have happened." When I eat something that I know is a trigger and then get diarrhea, it's obvious to me: "This is what I get for eating something I shouldn't have."

We can't blame ourselves for dropping a few steps along the way in this dance we do endlessly for our entire lives. Skipping exercise or eating a trigger food isn't actually the reason why I'm sick. I'm sick because I have a disease called endometriosis. I have tissue on my pelvic organs that shouldn't be there, causing high levels of inflammation that affect my full body and adhesions that cause my pelvic organs to fuse together. That is why I'm sick, and *none* of that is my fault. There's no step I can take and no lifestyle change that will cure endometriosis. Doing this intricate dance to try to keep myself feeling as well as I can is a fantastic thing I do for myself, but it's not going to ever change the underlying fact that I have a disease.

I'm only starting to understand this—sixteen years into the dance! Since high school, I've believed it was my fault I'm sick. Why?! Probably because of the stories my mind told me about my lack of worth, coupled with doctor after doctor declaring that I was in 'perfect health.' I was so young and impressionable when I first got sick—if there was nothing physically wrong with me, I had to be doing it to myself!

And once I saw that I could prevent flares if I danced with endometriosis, I felt a heavy burden on my shoulders to live the 'perfect' lifestyle, eat the 'perfect' diet, exercise the 'perfect' amount, so that I could avoid all of these flares. That led to me being obsessive with my health, afraid of food, and really rigid in my routines.

Is living in constant obsession healthy? No, it isn't. While it's empowering to take steps to avoid triggers and to follow a more personally fitting lifestyle that helps improve my quality of life, I can do so without the pressure and expectations that I've been putting on myself. There will be times when no matter how well I dance with endometriosis, I will have a flare. That's just the nature of this disease and how it affects the body. If I can come to terms with that, I can have a different relationship with endometriosis and with myself. If I have a flare—*when* I have a flare—I don't need to feel disappointed in myself, believe I'm a failure, or hate myself for not having tried harder. I can bring in the knowing that this isn't my fault.

For years, I have danced with endometriosis frantically and resentfully out of *fear* of having a flare. But now, I want to dance with endometriosis out of *love* and *care* for myself. When I change my dance partner from self-blame to self-compassion, my experience with this dance completely transforms. It no longer matters if I excel at the steps or not, but that I'm on the dance floor, making an effort to prevent flares where I can. Instead of feeling pressure, I can feel proud to be dancing as best as I can. This sometimes means stumbling, but other times it means flowing with grace across the dance floor. The dance no longer feels like an obligation but instead a choice I make every day so that I can have a better life with endometriosis.

Self-Reflection

- While taking care of ourselves and adopting more personally fitting habits can help us feel empowered in managing our symptoms, it can also feel like a burden on us. Do you ever feel pressure to take care of yourself to try to avoid triggering your symptoms? This could be self-imposed, from society, or a loved one.
- Do you feel an obligation to yourself to avoid certain foods or to have a specific lifestyle?
- Do you ever feel trapped in what you feel you 'have' to do to manage your symptoms?
- If you take any steps to manage your symptoms, do

you feel proud of yourself for taking those steps? If not, why not?

- How can you bring in compassion and understanding to the fact that having this disease isn't your fault, and you're doing the best you can right now?
- How can you take the pressure off of yourself?

42

IS HAPPINESS POSSIBLE?

On a two week road trip through Utah's national parks, we camped under the incredible stars. Each morning we woke with the dawn at five a.m. to witness the sky change from night to day in the most spectacular array of colors. I felt deeply moved seeing the sun rise out of the pink and orange clouds like a glowing ball of fire. "I'm here!" it tells the earth. "Wake up!" I watched in awe as silhouettes of arches and other rock formations millions of years old began to distinguish themselves out of the darkness. They had disappeared in the blackness of the night—blended together as one solid, indistinguishable mass—but were beginning to have their separate outlines again.

I have always loved sunrises. In high school, I used to drive thirty minutes on the weekend to watch the sun come up over the ocean. When the sunlight streams over the horizon, it reveals the colors, forms, and shapes that were always there in the night, just hidden in the darkness. The earth is quiet and still at such an early hour, full of beauty and hope. Every sunrise brings a new day; every day brings a new chance. A new chance to feel better, a new chance that circumstances will be different, a new chance to find happiness.

Sixteen years I have been searching for answers with my health; that's 5,840 sunrises. But in spite of these 5,840 new chances, I am still sick and also deeply unhappy. Things always seem to improve briefly before some weird random problem rears its ugly little head: endometriosis, interstitial cystitis, IBS, gastritis, fibromyalgia—and all the symptoms these bring. Routine activities like eating, sleeping, having sex, menstruating, and using the bathroom cause a variation of stabbing pain, constant pain, sharp pain, dull pain, unexpected pain, debilitating pain, burning pain, and nauseating pain. No matter how many times the sun rises, I never feel better. Nor do I find happiness.

My idea of happiness is intrinsically tied to my health. There are times when I think about what I would need from life to be happy: to successfully hold in my pee until I make it to the toilet, to feel full and nourished after eating instead of sick and nauseous. In contrast to the hell I'm currently living in, my 'heaven' would be a place where my body doesn't exist, where I never have to worry about eating food or using the bathroom again.

I'm working on separating my happiness from my health, so I've been meditating recently on my beliefs about their relationship. By watching objectively the thoughts that come to mind, I see that I've been confusing *deep* happiness with *fleeting* happiness—instead of distinguishing between the two. Fleeting happiness comes and goes with circumstances; it is that bright, happy energy that bursts out of me and makes me smile. But deep happiness is different; it doesn't depend on circumstances being one way or another, nor does it make me feel elated. To me, deep happiness is more like an internal sense of well-being, a state that I rest in and can approach the world from. It goes hand in hand with the peace that comes from accepting the things I cannot change. Deep happiness doesn't mean I won't be sad, upset, or heartbroken at times; it's not about pretending everything is fine when it isn't or repressing or pushing down the authentic emotions that I feel. There is no pressure to be happy all of the time—this is unrealistic and impossible anyway. This mindset welcomes all emotions into my life as a part of being human, but the key is that I don't get stuck in them nor live from them as I have been doing for the last decade.

For me, deep happiness is about feeling and working through the emotions that arise to specific situations, without judging them as good or bad, and once I have processed them, finding my way back to the resting state of peace. This state is built on the foundation I've been cultivating of gratitude and mindfulness and being present to the moment before me. To me, acceptance, calm, and peace are a huge component of deep happiness.

When I frame it like that, I can see that deep happiness isn't conditional on anything external—it's *inside* of me. It's another skill that can be cultivated and learned, just like gratitude and resilience. But where to start? I suppose a good start is this realization that my deep happiness is something I can intentionally take the reins of. After all, I've learned from 5,840 sunrises that happiness isn't just going to *happen* to me. I have to search inside myself to find it. I've recently begun this process by working on my negative self-talk, redefining my idea of meaning, and starting to let go of my attachment to what I want but can't have. I have lived for so long from the stories of 'I don't have enough', 'I'm not good enough', and 'I hate my life'—which has been a huge barrier in trying to find happiness.

It all starts with my beliefs. What if I changed my definition of happiness so that it didn't depend on my body or on me not having endometriosis? Because my happiness is currently conditional on my health, but I have a chronic disease, my story around happiness is: *I will never be happy.* What then? This belief becomes self-fulfilling and annihilates all chances of happiness. Since I don't believe it's possible, I don't even try for it, locking myself into a state of inaction. After all, why bother? I've told myself it's impossible anyway.

Studies suggest that we have a happiness 'set point' that determines our general level of happiness. Our happiness 'set point' is different for all of us and is said to be based on genetics and conditioning. But studies also suggest that we can change this set point with our thoughts, habits, and behaviors.[1] What we do matters, and our efforts can result in change. I've already seen this with both my physical and mental health—lifestyle and diet changes result in fewer flares; daily meditation results in a better tolerance for pain.

Can I set my happiness point to include having endometriosis and chronic pain? I've made a commitment to finding acceptance with my life. Today, I will make another important commitment—to discover how I can be happy with my life. And, hopefully, one will beget the other.

I feel a small flicker of life in my soul. It's the same hope I've felt whenever I've witnessed the sun rising before me. A new day, a new chance. The seed of a new mindset has been planted in me. It will need nurturing and cultivating; it will need time, practice, and repetition to grow. I may need to reach out to a mental health professional to help me move through my traumas. I may need to spend more time with my meditation teacher to really understand how to cultivate awareness. I may need to read more books on wisdom teachings to have them guide me or do more journaling to explore the depths of my subconscious beliefs. That's all part of the journey, and that's okay, now that I'm understanding that true happiness isn't out of reach for me.

I get up from the chair I'm sitting in and turn on the kettle to make myself a cup of tea. As I watch the water start to boil and the bubbles rise up in it, I think about how the water that was previously still and unmoving in the pot is now in motion. It's like the water has become alive, dancing with bubbles. I smile to myself. That kind of force is inside of me, too, and I think I just awakened it.

Self-Reflection

- What does happiness mean to you?
- Do you think happiness is a skill, intention, or commitment?
- Can you open to the possibility of being happy?
- Do you have any beliefs that are holding you back?
- Does your happiness currently depend on anything? What stands in the way of you being happy?
- Can you think of any steps you can commit yourself to taking to move your happiness set point?

43

I AM NOT BROKEN

To my body: my beautiful, fascinating, miraculous body,

I want you to know that I'm not angry with you anymore for the pain we've been in. You have been just as hurt as I have. Of course you are in pain, when your abdomen is filled with endometriosis, causing high levels of inflammation and organs to be fused together by adhesions.

To my beautiful, fascinating, miraculous body: I'm done hating you. I'm no longer going to wish I had a different body—you are a wonderful body. You have done me well on countless occasions. You have always been there for me.

My beautiful body, do you remember that time I cut my thumb opening a can of tuna and I needed five stitches? Thank you for healing that wound.

My beautiful body, do you remember that time I twisted my ankle and needed crutches for a week? Thank you for healing that sprain.

My beautiful body, do you remember that time I spilled hot

water on my thighs and the skin peeled off? Thank you for healing those burns.

My beautiful body, do you remember that time I had food poisoning? Thank you for healing from that bacterial infection.

To my beautiful, fascinating, miraculous body: thank you for carrying me through thirty-three years of life so far, through three surgeries, through thousands of hours of pain, through hundreds of doctor's appointments, through disappointment and shock and heartache, through love and joy and excitement. You have carried me through life in all its magnificence and ugliness, and I thank you for keeping me alive.

Thank you to my lungs, which bring in fresh air and provide oxygen to my blood supply, keeping me alive with every breath.

Thank you to my heart, which pumps my blood, moving nutrients to my cells from head to toe.

Thank you to my skin, which provides a barrier between my vital organs and the outside world; skin that feels the warmth of the sun's rays and the loving caress of human touch.

Thank you to my immune system, which protects me from viruses and bacteria.

Thank you to my liver, which detoxifies my blood, removing substances that would otherwise harm me.

Thank you to my digestive tract, which breaks down the food I eat, turning it into the energy I need to get out of bed every day and take part in all the amazing experiences of this world.

To my beautiful, fascinating, miraculous body: together, we have had some truly incredible times. You have allowed me to participate in this life in so many ways; you have let me express my creativity through song, dance, and art.

Thank you to my eyes, which take in gorgeous sunsets, stunning artwork, and the intricate shadows that the tree branches cast on the grass.

Thank you to my nose, which brings me the delicious aroma of cookies baking and the sweet whiff of spring flowers in the air.

Thank you to my brain, which ponders complex philosophy, imagines far-off lands while reading the pages of a novel, and intrigues me with creative ideas.

Thank you to my feet, which have taken me on adventures all over the world, giving me the opportunity to meet incredible people from many different cultures and gain new perspectives.

Thank you to my hands, which hold my loved ones' hands, pet my kitty's soft fur, and prepare nourishing meals for myself.

To my beautiful, fascinating, miraculous body, I finally understand that you have not betrayed me. We are not broken. We are beautifully and perfectly whole, and it's not our fault that we have endometriosis.

Self-Reflection

- Write a letter to thank your body. Think about the good things your body does for you.
- Think about the ways your body keeps you alive and the injuries that your body has healed.
- What emotions do you normally feel toward your body?
- Is your relationship with your body strained?
- In this letter, can you explore the idea of letting go of any hatred, anger, resentment, or fear you have toward your body?

44

SOCIAL STIGMA

While on summer break during my time teaching in Japan, I had the opportunity to travel to the neighboring country of Mongolia. It's a beautiful land of open fields, mountains, and desert. Once we arrived at the capital, my friend and I joined a ten-day tour with four other Western tourists who were also in their early twenties. Our local Mongolian tour guides took us into the remote countryside where there were no villages—or even roads! It was incredible to see how the guides knew the route only from their memory and recognition of the landscape. By day, we saw gorgeous valleys, rivers, and mountains, and in the evening we camped on the land of local herders. Their yurts were the only sign of human life among the hundreds of miles of open land.

Everything was going well until the third day. I was having a fantastic time, ecstatic to be on such an adventure, when my period unexpectedly came. It was two weeks early! I immediately panicked, hardly able to take a breath from the fear that now overcame me. I was only twenty-two and not yet skilled at carrying around my emergency period supply kit; I had no painkillers with me, nor sanitary supplies. Neither did the others I was with, and we were a full day's drive to the closest store.

I didn't know what else to do, so I asked the driver to stop the van. I went behind it and stuffed clean socks into my underwear. I got back in the van, and as we continued driving, that out-of-this-world pain rose up in my back. With no painkillers, there was nothing I could do but suffer in front of everyone.

I was trapped in a van, in the middle of hundreds of miles of open field, with a single friend and six total strangers. There was nothing but the land and us. There was *nowhere* to have any inkling of privacy. There was no bathroom stall to hide in, no private room to escape to, nothing except sheep and grass.

Since we were all shoulder to shoulder in the van, I changed with someone to be in the far seat, slumping against the window. The pain, the pain. I tried as best I could to bear it in silence, but the pain was too intense. My face twisted up in agony as everyone uneasily listened to me moan and sob and howl. We were all young; even our two Mongolian guides probably weren't older than late twenties, and no one knew what to do. My friend suggested I cover my head with a jacket to have some privacy, and they turned the car stereo up to try and drown out my cries.

Next came the back-to-back waves of vomiting and diarrhea. At the first urge, I asked them to stop the van. The only privacy among the beautiful, vast green valley that stretched for miles in every direction was behind the van. While my friend and the six strangers waited in it, their music blaring, I took my pants and underwear off and got down on my hands and knees—the pain was unbearable and I was in no condition to squat. I felt like an animal, puking, having diarrhea, and writhing in pain on the grass next to my excretions, clutching my back in agony.

Every twenty minutes or so, the tour guide would pop his head out the window and, without looking, gently ask if I would need much longer. We were on a schedule, and in the uninhabited countryside without electricity, streetlights, or even roads, where they used the familiarity of the land to cross hundreds of miles, we would be stranded if we didn't arrive before nightfall to the yurt of the people we were camping with.

An hour later, my body finally stopped spasming and I was able to get back in the van. Everyone sat in awkward silence for the rest of the ride. No one put a loving hand on my arm and asked if I was okay; no one gave me a hug for the hell I had just been (and was still going) through. They didn't know what to do, and neither did I. I put the jacket back over my head so they couldn't see the tears of defeat and shame that streamed down my face. I felt like an outcast, like I could never look any of them in the eyes again.

What does endometriosis often bring us? Trauma. Social stigma. Loneliness.

Looking back, my heart breaks for myself in that situation. It's one of dozens of flares that I've had in public. When confronted with a person in such a high level of pain, most people don't know how to help. Many don't have any experience in showing compassion for another suffering human being, so they get scared, uncomfortable, or freaked out.

Sometimes, when I'm rolling around in pain on the sidewalk, in a restaurant, or at work, people have called an ambulance; other times, they have just stood there rubbernecking with their curious eyes as if I were an attraction in a zoo. It's impossible to escape the prying eyes, the morbid stares, the raised eyebrows, the eyerolls, the looks of disgust, the scrutiny, the judgmental accusations of "What's *wrong* with you?"

As I sit today with my memories, my breath becomes shallow, my face feels hot, and my stomach tightens. I can feel the deep shame I felt in those moments, and I feel sick from reliving it, sick from the thought that it happened in the first place. I sigh heavily and loudly, which always is therapeutic to me.

Shame. It's been corroding me for years. There's so much in my life. It's an invisible cloak that's been suffocating me but I've only just noticed I am wearing it. As I examine its fibers, I wonder how I even came to put on this cloak of shame in the first place.

And if I can learn why I put it on, then can I learn to take it off again?

Like many things in life, the reasons are complex. Endometriosis can bring with it issues like incontinence or heavy menstrual bleeding, which historically has been considered to be disgusting by society. Menstruation is still thought of as taboo in many parts of the world, and in many cultures, it remains a dirty and impure event. Even though it's a natural bodily process connected to the beautiful ability to create life, it remains poorly understood by many and therefore, judged.

Then there is society's tendency to look down on anything that's considered 'weak', such as illness, losing control of our body, or even the natural process of aging. In the competitive, individualistic United States, we have been raised with these background ideas of survival of the fittest, being strong, a 'dog eat dog' world. If we don't fit in, we may be bullied or ostracised, and unlike what the movies show us, it isn't just in high school.

And endometriosis certainly makes it difficult to fit in. Apart from 'causing a scene' in public during a flare, there's the daily fatigue, pain, nausea, and brain fog, which can cause me to walk slowly, speak quietly to conserve energy, or forget things. This can lead to misunderstandings, assumptions, and cruel comments from others. There have been so many times when I've just wanted to disappear. In those moments, if only the earth would just swallow me up.

But it can't, so shame swallows me up instead.

In my curiosity and investigation into my shame, I see how intertwined it is with my self-worth. Its cloak sits over another cloak weaved with the fabric of "I'm a terrible person." Both are clasped with buttons made of self-judgment and criticism.

Little by little, I'm learning to sit with my shame, to feel how it burns my cheeks and turns my stomach. I'm working on allowing it to be: staying present with the heat, nausea, and heaviness, and holding it with compassion and acceptance. The more I do this, the more the shame dissolves. I'm discovering that underneath the shame, there is an incredible amount of strength to have gotten through these moments. In Mongolia, I was in a vulnerable, scary, overwhelming situation. It was a bad situation—but I wasn't in it because I am a bad person. I was in it because I have endometriosis, and this illness can cause spontaneous, incapacitating flares that make a person lose control of their body.

Looking past my shame, I can see that someone who lives with endometriosis is actually the opposite of weak. What we've been through, both individually and collectively as people with endometriosis—the flares, the surgeries, the misunderstandings and judgments of others, the doctor's appointments, the pain, and the emotional turmoil of it all—is evidence of our incredible courage and resilience.

Self-Reflection

- Do you feel social stigma toward any aspects of your illness?
- Have you had any situations because of your illness that caused you to feel ashamed or mortified? What happened?
- Does your illness ever make you feel like you are 'weak' or 'less than' others?
- Have others ever made you feel this way?

- What is underneath your 'cloak' of shame? Are there fears of being abandoned, rejected, or unloved?
- How does your level of shame tie in with your self-esteem? Are they connected?
- Can you think of times you've been courageous or resilient—perhaps through flares, surgeries, getting through the emotional turmoil?
- If you feel embarrassed about your illness in the future, try to remember these times.

45

MAKING TIME FOR A MOMENT OF CALM

As I eat my breakfast, I take a moment to think about my day today. In Japan, I walked everywhere and taught English in a classroom filled with windows. Now that I'm living in the US again, I get in my car and sit in traffic in order to get to work, where I will answer emails and calls in a small cubicle all day, then get back in my car and drive home. Once I arrive home, it will already be dark due to these short winter hours of sunlight. I am separate from the living world all day, in my boxes: my apartment, my car, my cubicle.

Not only has it been ages since I've gotten outside, but I also haven't been honoring the promise that I made to myself to prioritize finding a moment of joy each day. I've fallen prey to the busy modern lifestyle, rushing from here to there. I'm over-committed to self-imposed social obligations and spending way too many hours on an ever lengthening to-do list. Joy has been crowded out by its enemy: busyness. I'm sacrificing more than my time—I'm sacrificing my mental health along with it.

When I'm stressed and rushed, I'm not present. I'm usually impatient, frustrated, or thinking of the next task I have to do. Moving at an accelerated pace, there's no time to notice the sacred around me—the morning dew shining on the grass, a beam of sunlight coming in through the window, the song of a bird, the unexpected kindness of a stranger, a warm drink, a smile, a laugh, the excitement of receiving a card in the mail.

Not only have I stopped paying attention to the simple moments and the joy they bring, but I've cut out the meaningful activities that I had committed to building into my life. In the last month, I haven't taken any steps for my emotional well-being. I have 'no time' to paint, read, or meditate. Since I've moved back to the US, I've really been struggling with intentionally taking the time to relax and do self-care.

I miss how much I used to walk everywhere when I lived in Japan. What if I commit right now to taking a walk outside every single day for fifteen minutes? It's just enough time to get a little fresh air, feel the crispness of the cold on my face, or enjoy the sounds of the rain pattering on my umbrella. It's so easy to get 'caught up in life' and overlook the importance of time for myself, but that's okay—I'll try again, and this time I'll make a plan. When I arrive home from work, before I even go inside, I will stroll around the block. This way, I'm already wearing my shoes and coat, and it will become a part of my regular routine. It will be revitalizing to end the workday doing something for me, to walk off any work stress and transition into my evening at home. It's such a simple act, yet as I've been learning, it's often these small things that can completely change the tone of our life.

Self-Reflection

- Is self-care important to you?
- What helps you take care of your mental health?
- Do you prioritize activities that help your emotional

well-being, or do you find you are too busy to devote that time to yourself?

- If the latter, think about why you are too busy. Can you examine the importance of the reasons why you are too busy? Are all of your reasons for being too busy actually as important as they seem?
- Think about your schedule in general. Do you have unwanted obligations or to-do list 'priorities' that actually aren't priorities?
- Can any be cut down or eliminated from your schedule, leaving you more time to do the activities that actually bring you joy?

46

AT THE HANDS OF FATE

One day, about halfway through my teaching post in the village in the Amazon, I was going to fly out to the closest town to get more supplies. I was excited at the thought of enjoying my first hot shower in months, sleeping in a hotel room without the tarantulas, crickets, and cockroaches that cohabited my cabin with me, and buying some dark chocolate at the local store.

I walked up to a hut on the hillside, where one of my students and her family lived. There wouldn't be much time to catch the small nine-seater cargo plane when it came, and their lodging was fifteen minutes closer to the airstrip than my cabin was. As soon as I heard the drone of the airplane motor overhead, I would need to rush to the airstrip. Since there was no way I was going to run there and risk wearing myself out from fatigue or invoking a flare, I needed to be closer so that I could walk at a normal pace and still arrive quickly. The plane took off again about about thirty minutes after it landed. There was no real schedule: the plane came sometime on Tuesdays, usually in the morning, and it all depended on the weather. If it was raining or if the ground was still muddy from previous rain, the dirt airstrip became treacherously slick and the plane wouldn't risk landing, even if it had flown for the fifty minutes from town! It would turn around, return to the town, and try again in the next day or two if conditions permitted.

My student was home, along with her sisters and mother. They invited me in, and we began chatting. "I'm leaving the village today," I told them.

Her mother smiled, "Si Dios quiere." *God willing.*

I heard this phrase often here: Si Dios quiere—God willing. I've come to love this phrase. Back in US culture, it might seem emotionally charged or inappropriate to those who are not religious, but here in the rainforest where the elements ruled, it always seemed perfectly fitting. The phrase itself was open to interpretation; it could be meant literally, "if God will have it", but here, it also takes on a less religious context as a simple proverb, "if it's meant to be, if the universe allows, if circumstances permit."

I personally see it as a helpful phrase to remind myself of that which I cannot control. Right then, I couldn't control the rain. I had no power over whether the plane would come or not. It was completely out of my hands, and instead in the hands of fate, under the power of cause and effect. If it didn't rain, the plane would come; as fate would have it, I'd leave the village. If it started to rain, the plane wouldn't come; as fate would have it, my hot shower and dark chocolate would wait another day.

Fate. The word conjures up an image of the mythology of three Greek Moirai—the Fates Atropos, Clotho, and Lachesis—in the sky, weaving our future in their great tapestry that not even the powerful Zeus, the king of the Greek Gods, could change the outcome of.

In my mind, fate is another way to refer to what cannot be changed. Like that moment waiting for the plane, events would unfold as they would, unable to be influenced by a mere mortal like me. That's not to say I do nothing. I still make every effort to influence what I can to take responsibility for my life and actively shape it—like walking up to this hut to be much closer to the airstrip, giving me a better chance at catching the plane if it did indeed come to the village.

It's the same with my illness. I put in a lot of effort daily to positively affect how I feel. I research heavily before making treatment decisions, I take care of myself through diet and lifestyle, I prepare for my period and debilitating pain by cooking meals beforehand. But ultimately, there is so much that is out of my control. I don't know what side effects a new medication will actually cause me, or if I will have a flare when I leave the house, or what complications I might have from surgery. As human beings, we tend to dislike that which we can't control. When the outcome is uncertain, it often leads to great fear and anxiety.

What is one to do, then? Make the best effort to have the best outcome but know that in the end, what will be will be? If I cannot control how a situation turns out, what can I control? Myself. My reaction to the situation. The way I handle it. The way I feel about it. If I choose to learn from it.

Of course, this is easier said than done. I'm trying though, because I can see that my mindset is powerful. It can cause me to crumble over the smallest troubles or stand tall in front of monumental obstacles. I am embarrassed to recall how poorly I handled the majority of my past situations. It's hard to let go of the shame and regret I feel for all the ways I've snapped at people in anger, complained incessantly instead of taking action, or used unhealthy coping mechanisms to try and escape my challenges.

I can't go back in time to take back the way I've led my life, but I can focus on the way I'm living it now. I can set intentions, learn tools for coping, and work toward having a new perspective. This part of my destiny—the person I want to be—is not in the hands of the Fates but is up to me to cultivate.

Did the plane come that day? It did. But as I waited in the hut, listening carefully for the drone of the approaching plane, I decided that even if it didn't, I would use those circumstances to practice letting go of what I wanted. Can I embrace what is out of my control? It was in that moment that I realized something that has helped guide me through the difficult, unwelcome times: Perhaps, as a person with endometriosis, my fate isn't to have an easy life, but to have one that teaches me and challenges me to grow.

Self-Reflection

- What does fate mean to you?
- How much control do you think we have over our lives?
- Where do you have control over your illness?
- What are you doing to play an active role in how you feel?
- Do you think we are in control of our reactions to the things that happen to us?
- How do you feel when you don't know how the outcome of something will be?

47

TAPED UP LIKE A VASE

Note: This essay contains descriptions of pain that some readers may find upsetting.

A creative writing piece about my period.

I woke up to the overwhelming smell of ash. I blinked groggily. Daylight was streaming into the room. I soon realized that I was on the floor. The bed had collapsed, the frame in pieces all over the room. The mattress was missing huge chunks, and some coils had sprung out. The blanket was in tatters; the pillow a smoldering piece of cloth.

The side table was gone too. What's going on? Shards of wood were mixed in with the broken glass where the lamp had shattered into thousands of pieces on the floor.

The room was in chaos, and I was right in the middle of the mess. There were jagged shards of glass in my side, and my right arm was pinned down by a heavy piece of the wooden bedframe. Some cotton from inside my pillow was dried to the blood between my legs; my abdomen had a huge, gaping hole in it.

Oh.

I remembered now. My period came yesterday. The hole is where the grenade went off in my uterus.

I lay there, surveying the scene. The damage was shocking. I noticed my clock upside down across the room, the display off. I sighed. I had no idea what time it was, but today was Monday, so I had to go to work. I struggled to get up, slowly, weak from the pain, weighed down by my responsibilities. My head was pounding, probably from dehydration. My throat burned from the throwing up I did yesterday, and oh, how my abdomen ached.

I looked down at myself. I couldn't go to work with this massive hole in my body. I need to fill it with something. I looked around the room in a daze. No wonder why I felt so empty. Little pieces of my soul were everywhere, ripped off of me in the blast. I picked up a piece of my heart lying lifelessly under the rubble and brushed the ash off it. There was another heart fragment in the wall, and I struggled to lift one of the bedposts off what remained of my dignity.

With several pieces of myself gathered up in my hands, I did my best to shove them back into the hole in my abdomen. *It's not complete,* I thought. *I'm not complete, but it will have to do.* It's good enough to get me through the day, and that's all I need right now. Where is the tape? There it was in the corner of the room, the same place I had left it last month when this happened. I hurried to wrap myself with it so that none of the pieces would fall out. Okay, good enough.

I threw on a baggy shirt so no one would notice the uneven edges of my makeshift belly. I dabbed a little concealer on my dark eye circles and grabbed my keys, taking one last look in the mirror. The person who stared back at me looked weak, thin, a little shaken—a traumatized shadow of the person that I was just a few days ago, before the explosion. "You can do this," I said out loud. It's only eight hours, and then, when the day is over, you can crawl home to rest and try to heal.

I took a ragged deep breath and walked out the door. After a moment, I stopped and went back inside. I grabbed the tape and put it in my purse, just in case any of the pieces come apart during the day.

Self-Reflection

Do you ever feel like you are barely holding yourself together?

Think of something that is causing you to suffer right now or recently in the past. Acknowledge that at this moment (or very recently) you are suffering. Say to yourself, "I am suffering because ________ (for example, I have abdominal pain, a friend dismissed my symptoms, I'm confused about treatment, I have endo)."

Now, think about how other humans worldwide are suffering from this exact same thing. As you breathe in, do so knowing that many other people worldwide are suffering just like you. This may feel undesirable, difficult, or overwhelming the first few times you do this; it may even bring you to tears. How does it feel as you realize the suffering of others with each inhale? Does the breath feel heavy? Does the breath catch in your throat?

As you breathe out, breathe out loving-kindness, relief, comfort, peace, and love for these people who are suffering, including yourself. How does it feel as you send this love and compassion to them? Does your exhale feel different than the inhale? Does it feel light, warm, cool, powerful, revitalizing?

Set a timer and practice this for three minutes.

Was it difficult to do this practice? Do you think doing it in your moments of suffering will help you to feel less alone, sit better with suffering, or better awaken your sense of compassion for others?

If you would like to learn more about this practice, it was adapted from a meditation practice called *Tonglen*.

48

I CAN HANDLE WHAT I FEEL

I'm in a high level of pain almost every day. The grief I feel for what I've lost because of this illness crushes my heart.

On my way home from a long draining workday due to the high level of pain I was in, I have to keep telling myself to keep my eyes on the road. As I drive on a back country road, with no other cars in sight and where no one can see me, I have a breakdown, screaming over and over about my life. "Make the pain go away, make my life simple again. Please help me please I can't do this I can't I don't want to I just can't." I drive recklessly, wailing at the top of my lungs. Suddenly, I hear myself, and it startles me that these sounds are coming from my throat.

Distressed, I pull over, screeching to a halt three inches from a tree. A part of me feels relief for not having crashed my car, another part of me wishes that I had so that I could end my life and this suffering. I push the door open and collapse on my knees on the damp ground, sobbing about how much I hate this life.

I'm not okay.

Fully immersed in my inconsolable grief, I cry in a ball on the ground next to my car. After several minutes, I practice putting a name to these overwhelming feelings: "Falling apart," I whisper. "Hopelessness. Desperation. It's okay..." I soothe myself, wrapping my arms around my knees. "It's okay to feel this."

Society has taught many of us to repress our emotions: to put on a smile even if you are feeling sad; to answer the question "how are you?" with "I'm fine" even when you are anything but fine; to push yourself to find the positive, even if in reality, the situation may be absolutely awful with nothing positive to be found. Because of this, many of us don't know how to feel our emotions. We run away from them, find them uncomfortable, or think there is something wrong with us if we are not experiencing 'positive' emotions 24/7.

But who decided that emotions are 'positive' or 'negative'? Why do we have to put them into these binary categories, implying that one emotion is good while another is bad? This isn't the case at all. Our emotions are natural, necessary responses to our life situations; they are states of energy that can communicate to us if only we can welcome them and look deeper. For example, my grief shows me how much I am holding onto the fact that I want my life back—the one I had without pain, without special diets, without diarrhea, without surgeries, without medications.

But that life isn't coming back, at least not as it was. And right now, what my personal sadness is telling me is that I need to mourn and cry to help me adjust. As for my distressing suicidal ideation,[1] in my case, it's not an urge to die at all but rather a realization that I cannot live like this any longer. My life is currently intolerable and some things need to change—to 'die', metaphorically speaking—such as my tendency to identify as a victim of my circumstances and the pressure I put on myself to always be 'fine.'

I have a habit of feeling guilty and disappointed in myself for the sadness, anger, or whatever supposedly 'negative' emotion

I'm feeling, as if it were unacceptable to feel this way. I'm continuously shooting myself with the second arrow that the Buddha spoke of, adding an unneeded extra layer of judgment and suffering to my current suffering. Slowly though, I'm starting to understand that there is nothing unacceptable about fully feeling my feelings. They are not good or bad—they make up the whole spectrum of being human.

What's more, my feelings are passing states, and when I treat them as such, they do eventually pass. Ironically, during the years that I actively avoided my sadness through distracting myself with movies, the internet, shopping, and other unhealthy coping mechanisms, I was actually stuck in it. My sadness was always lingering in the background, never fully seen or addressed but always weighing me down.

Now, when sadness or other emotions come, I welcome them. It's not easy, but I open the door and 'invite them in for tea.' I learned this from a story about the Buddha. Whenever Mara, the Demon God of the shadow, would attack the Buddha with troubling thoughts and emotions, the Buddha would acknowledge Mara and invite him to tea, being with him instead of avoiding him. Mara would visit and then take his leave.

I'm learning to do this with my own emotions. When sadness knocks on the door, I open it and widely and say, "Hello, my friend. What message do you have for me?" When anger, loneliness, or another 'negative' emotion shows up, I do the same. They visit and leave again, rather than knocking constantly at the door every day while I try to hide or push them away. Actually being with my emotions allows me to process and work through them. I think about the situation, why I feel this way, and what the emotion is trying to tell me—something I can't do when I'm trying to run away from it! And the more I 'drink tea' with my emotions, the more I'm getting familiar and comfortable with them. They feel less overwhelming, less intense, and less dreadful to be with than they once did. I'm gaining confidence in myself to be with all of my emotions —now I know that I *am* capable of holding them and that they will pass.

This is such a beautiful and life-changing gift to myself: learning that even when I feel broken, even when things fall apart, I *can* be there for myself. I can count on myself; I can be kind and compassionate with myself, and help myself get through it.

Self-Reflection

Go through the following emotions one by one and recall a time in your life when you felt each of these different feelings: **sadness, joy, disappointment, happiness, anger**. They don't have to be big events—they can be, but they can also be from simple moments. For example, 'I felt sadness when my close friend forgot to wish me a happy birthday.' Write out a few sentences about each experience you had that brought up that emotion.

- Look back at each example, asking yourself the following questions for each one: How was it to have that feeling? For example, was it nice to experience it, uncomfortable, scary, overwhelming?
- How long did that feeling last?[2]
- Did you want that feeling to go away, or did you want to hang on to it forever?
- Did you judge yourself for having that feeling?

49

I FORGIVE MYSELF

Guilt.
It permeates my being.

Guilt for breaking plans again because I was sick.

Guilt for deciding not to fly home for my mom's sixty-fifth birthday party because traveling makes me sick.

Guilt for getting my period during the week of my best friend's wedding and missing her special day.

Guilt that sex is painful so I'm not able to share that with my partner.

Guilt for feeling sorry for myself when so many people worldwide are in much worse situations than mine.

Guilt for not accomplishing everything I wanted to today and instead laying in bed with a flare.

Guilt. Being sick isn't something we have 'done' wrong, so why do I feel I'm a bad person and letting everyone down, including myself?

Guilt can be a helpful emotion: a moral compass, a teacher of right and wrong—but not in this case. Applied to my illness, this guilt is toxic and useless. Taking a step back from my life and watching my thoughts around my guilt, I see it's arising out of fear, not out of wrongdoing. After all, it's not wrong to take care of myself, stay in, or say no. But I have a lot of insecurity about being liked by others. I put a lot of pressure on myself to please everyone so that they don't dislike or abandon me. I push myself to 'keep up' with a society that doesn't value rest at all, that has sayings like "You can sleep when you are dead" and "Time is money".

Guilt is a mindset that I live from. It's eating away at me and driving me to hate myself. I am trying to transform it into self-compassion and forgiveness by changing the way I speak to myself.

When I feel like a disappointment for cancelling plans and that familiar guilt washes over me, I'm trying to comfort that part of me that's scared my friends will stop inviting me out: "Don't worry, Amy, there will be future plans. I'm proud of you for recognizing that you need to rest."

When feelings of inadequacy rise up as I tell my supervisor that I need to work from home today due to a flare, I'm trying to reassure that part of me that's scared I'm going to lose my job: "It's okay to ask for these accommodations. You are a good worker, and you are justified in needing them."

What I feel like a failure because I'm in too much pain to have sex, I'm trying to soothe that part of me that's scared my partner will leave me: "It's okay that you can't always have sex. Just as you love simply being with your partner, they love simply being with you."

When I feel unproductive because I'm choosing to value rest instead of pushing myself to complete some task on my to-do list, I'm trying to convince that part of me that's scared I'm worthless: "Your value isn't in all you *do*—it's in who you *are.* Society has conditioned you to believe you have to always be busy, but this isn't true; you are allowed to slow down and rest."

Right now, I'm telling myself these statements, but I can't yet bring myself to believe them, even though I know on an intellectual level that they are true. It's hard to really believe them because they conflict with my long-held, subconscious beliefs that I should always be agreeable, productive, and not do anything that could bother other people. But my beliefs are making me miserable and sicker because they cause me to ignore what my body truly needs. On one level, I can recognize that, but it will take practice to feel comfortable making decisions that are in my best interest, since that's not what I'm used to doing. For me, this is a huge component in finding peace with endometriosis. How can I ever accept this disease if I can't accept myself and how I deal with the situations it puts me in?

And now? I sit here now pondering this and decide it's as good a time as any to begin.

I make a list of some different situations I've felt guilty for in relation to endometriosis. I take twenty minutes to write down everything that comes to mind, and the list has more than thirty situations that I've felt guilty about—and that I still feel guilty about. Some of them happened ten years ago, yet here they are on this list because the memories still stand out in my mind. As I glance over the paper, I immediately find myself judging it —*here is the evidence that I am indeed an awful person. No wonder why I am sick.*

"Self-blame," I say out loud, trying to break the trance of my subconscious reaction of criticizing myself. I put my hand on my heart and take a deep breath. "You are a good person. We all do things we feel bad about." I let that sink in for a minute, then exhale a long sigh. We *all* do things we feel bad about, but that doesn't make us inherently bad people.

I start to look over my list, taking each incident one at a time. I examine each 'terrible' act in detail, asking myself questions like: What happened? Could I have done something differently? Did I make the best choice for myself at the time? Why do I feel bad about what happened? Did I actually hurt someone or even lose them as a friend, or am I just needlessly worrying that I did?

Each time feelings of guilt and inadequacy come up, I take a deep breath and remind myself, "You are a good person. We all do things we feel bad about."

Ironically, as I go over the situations and circumstances, I see that in most cases, I would have made the same decisions. However, what I would have liked was to communicate better: to not get angry, upset, or start crying. Better communication can lead to fewer misunderstandings and fewer hurt feelings.

In an attempt to let go of my guilt, I decide to write a letter to each person I may have hurt in those various situations. I start with my mother:

Dear Mom,

I'm sorry that I missed your sixty-fifth birthday. I feel awful that I wasn't there to celebrate that milestone with you. I don't want you to think that I missed your party because it wasn't important to me—you are so extremely important to me and I love you so much.

I want to thank you for understanding that I couldn't make it to the celebration because it's difficult on my body to travel because of my endometriosis and the flares traveling causes me. I want you to know that I didn't make the decision lightly. I thought about it for a long time but in the end decided that I had to make the best decision for my health.

It hurt me to not be able to be with you on your special day, and I know it was disappointing I wasn't there. I'm really sorry I missed it. I love you, and I thank you for the love you give me.

Over the course of a month, I write over a dozen letters to people for situations, both big and small, that have been eating away at me. The letter to my partner is seven pages long, as he is the one I felt guilty around the most. I don't send the letters; I just place them in a drawer when I'm done writing them. Maybe I will send them one day, but most likely not. These cathartic letters are for me, a way to look for forgiveness and understanding of myself. I feel many of the wounds in my soul healing while I write the letters, as I deeply understand that my intentions have always been honest and caring toward others. Nothing I have done was with malintent. Of course, that doesn't mean that the way I acted at times didn't hurt others. Rather, it helps me bring in kindness for myself and understand that I don't need to keep feeling guilty a decade later for my mistakes. Pointing my finger at myself in blame and continuing to punish myself won't change the past, but bringing in compassion and awareness can help me change the future.

The last letter I write—and the hardest one—is the letter to myself:

Dear Amy,

Do you remember that time that you were too fatigued, too sick, in too much pain? You remember that you snapped at your friend, you cancelled those plans, you didn't stand up for yourself? It's okay. It's all okay. You're living with an illness that affects everything you do, and you're doing the best you can. You're handling it as well as anyone could handle chronic pain, endless doctor's appointments, and life-altering fatigue. You were so young when you got sick. You've been so scared of your periods, of loved ones getting tired of you, of never feeling better. Can you see how difficult things are? Can you recognize how hard you are trying? Can you understand that no one is perfect? It's not your fault you're sick—not at all. You're not a disappointment, undeserving, or unlovable.

I sit with this for several minutes, tears pouring down my face. The guilt fades somewhat and compassion for myself floods my heart. I have a deep realization that all of this time, I have been suffering. I am *still* suffering. I bring my pen back to the page, and slowly begin to write: *I forgive.* I feel incredibly uncomfortable as I write this, like what I'm writing is wrong or ridiculous. I sit there with these sensations, with the tightness in my throat and the slight nausea in my stomach. I focus on my breath, breathing slowly and deeply, as I write the last word letter by letter, pausing for a few breaths in between each letter: *m...y...s...e...l...f.*

The words on the paper stare back at me: *I forgive myself.* It's not entirely true yet, but realizing that I need to write those words, and actually doing so, is a huge step in the right direction.

Self-Reflection

- Do you ever feel guilty or like you're a disappointment or a failure because of the limitations of your illness?
- Do you ever feel like the decisions you've made to prioritize your health have hurt the feelings of others?
- Think of a time when you felt like this, and write a letter to that person. What happened? Why do you think the person was hurt? Would you have said or done differently if put in that situation today? Remember, you don't need to send this letter and you can delete/shred it when you are finished.
- Now, can you write a letter to yourself for a time that you felt like you let yourself down? Can you find compassion, understanding, and forgiveness for yourself and how difficult it is to live with endometriosis? Can you write 'I forgive myself'—and try your best to mean it?

50

THE WISDOM OF A BUTTERFLY

I sit on the porch. Saturday stretches before me. The sun came up a short while ago; its light is still weak and the shadows long. The day is not yet choked in heat. Time doesn't exist, and it doesn't need to. Today, there is no schedule to follow, no appointments, no meetings, no place at all that I have to be. The warm breeze passes over me, bringing with it a sense of freedom. Hours from now, the sun will take its rest from the sky and I, too, shall sleep. But between now and then, there is only this present moment. A chance to just be.

A butterfly floats by on the gentle breeze, landing on one of the flowers in the planter in front of me. Its pearl wings contrast stunningly against the vivid red flower. Butterflies always look relaxed. In spite of the fact that they only live a short time on this earth—many species of butterflies live for just two weeks—I bet they don't spend that time feeling rushed or anxious, worrying if they will make it to this or that flower on time, or if they will have enough hours in the day to get to all the flowers on their to-do list.

Lucky them! They don't have their minds to trap them in their anxieties and distractions. Instead, they can fully live their two weeks on this earth, appreciating their sensations instead of being stuck in their heads. They are not being swept off to another moment by their thoughts, missing what's right in front of them. Maybe two weeks isn't that short of time when you're actually *being*. In just a moment, you can experience so much. The butterfly can taste the sweetness of the nectar on its tongue, smell the aroma of the flower, and feel the warmth of the sun on its wings. Just as the hours stretch before me today, maybe those two weeks of a butterfly's life are experienced so deeply that time feels eternal.

If a butterfly could give a parting word at the end of their lifespan, would they lament, "Oh, what a short time I was given on this earth"? Or instead would they proudly proclaim, "What a beautiful life I have lived"?

What will *I* think when I get to the end of my life? I have spent over a decade actively hating my life, my body, and my illness. I don't want to get to my deathbed angry and bitter with the same feelings that have been my only reality for these past years. Can I let go of my poisonous expectations of what my life 'should' be—of what I want my life to be—and instead be with my life for exactly how it is?

Do the butterflies cry when it rains because they can't visit any flowers until it stops? The rain is dangerous for them; raindrops can knock them out of the sky and injure them, and the cool air can make it impossible to fly. So butterflies take refuge during a storm. They wait patiently, and then, when the storm ends, they emerge from hiding within minutes to land in the mud to take in its salts and minerals. They don't lament the hours they 'lost' to the rain. If they were able to speak, surely they would not say "How unfair. My life is only fourteen days, and during three of them there was a storm and I couldn't fly!"

How much I can learn from a butterfly. Even with the storms, even with all the days I 'lose' to chronic pain and illness, life can still be fulfilling and beautiful. If I can continue to adapt this mindset on a deep level instead of just contemplating it, I'm sure I will experience more positive emotions in my life.

I imagine myself as a butterfly flying with the kaleidoscope[1] and experiencing a sense of freedom. I would have bright blue wings and flutter carefree in the breeze, dropping in on this flower and that flower to drink its sweet nectar. I'd have no worries, no anxieties, no fears, no judgments. Instead, I'd have the calm presence that comes from being in the moment. When my two weeks pass, my wings that allowed me to travel so freely would turn back to dust. I would become one with the earth again, just as I had been before my beautiful life arose.

Death. It *will* come for me, as it will for all of us. It's easy to forget or push that out of my mind, but it became very real to me when my friend passed away. I can no longer deny that one day my life will end. This inevitable fate has become my reminder to cherish this fleeting existence as the treasure that it is. I've been asking myself often, *What matters to me?* The answers to that question are now guiding the way that I live.

For most of my life, I have lacked clarity. I've felt lost, aimless, and have given importance to the unimportant: my appearance, material goods, my popularity. All of that seems so trivial to me now as I shift toward new values: to have gratitude, help others, be present, awaken from the stories I tell myself, and live from a place of openness and love. Part of me wants to cringe when I think about what I used to care about, but what good would cringing do? It won't change the past. It won't help me live better now. All self-judgment does is poison the present. It's more helpful to bring compassion to the past and understand that I cared about the superficial because that's what I learned through culture, advertising, TV, and countless other influences. My 'unwanted' past actually led me to where I am right now—to be a person who is transforming her life to align her actions and intentions with her new values. I'm happy with who I'm becoming and the direction I'm heading. Since that's the case, it seems almost silly to keep feeling unhappy and embarrassed about my past. But, letting go takes time.

What a gift that I have more than two weeks on this earth, that I have ample time to grow, change, and mature. I've already had thirty-three years, which has gone by in a flash. Will I get another thirty-three years of life? Will they go by just as quickly? The wise butterfly on the flower before me gently flaps its wings and flies away toward the treeline. I suppose the real question isn't how much time I have left in this life, but rather, how can I live fully during the time I have?

Self-Reflection

- If you had only two weeks left to live, what would you want to do?
- Who would you spend that time with? Is there some truth you would speak to someone?
- Would you go somewhere special?
- Look over what you just wrote, keeping in mind the present. What matters to you?
- Are you living in alignment with your values?
- How does it make you feel to know that you have more time on this earth?
- Does it make you want to commit to spending more time with loved ones, speaking any truths, working less, or some other change?
- Starting right now, can you begin changing the way you are living?

51

A BEAUTIFUL GIFT

The more I practice, the easier it's getting to notice the times:

when I wake up with the amazing feeling of energy.
when I bend over to put on my socks and no pain shoots through my abdomen.
when I have a bowel movement without crying out in pain.
when I sleep through the night and don't get up three times to go pee.
when I walk up the stairs to my apartment and my legs don't burn from fatigue.
when I eat food and it doesn't cause bloating or gas.
when I don't have brain fog and can think sharply.
when the relentless nausea goes down and the overwhelming discomfort fades.

I'm focusing more on the moments (although infrequent) when I'm *not* in pain. They are little gifts my body gives me throughout the day—ordinary but beautiful moments that I used to take for granted. Sometimes, it's only a few seconds that I have relief, but I bring forth all of my awareness to the moment and savor it.

Self-Reflection

Make an effort today to notice three beautiful moments related to your health that you normally wouldn't have noticed. They can be very small, such as, 'for a few minutes I had no pain' or 'I ate a bite of food and didn't feel sick'.

Do you think you can commit to noticing at least three things per day from now forward? Perhaps you can begin a habit that when you go to sleep each night, you tell yourself your three things or write them down.

52

THE INFURIATING FLOWER

I sit on the meditation cushion trying to focus on my breath, but it seems impossible today. I'm thinking nonstop about the visit I had with the gynecologist yesterday, and I can't tell if I'm obsessing and ruminating over it, which I tend to do, or if my persistent thoughts about the visit are actually helping me process it.

A wave of anger comes over me. It's so strong it chokes me, and I find it hard to breathe. My heart beats quicker in my chest; I decide to take a break from trying to meditate and get some air. I put on my shoes and a light jacket and go outside. The ground is wet; it has been raining, and threatening clouds still loom overhead. I walk down the sidewalk, stopping in front of a large bush whose fuchsia flowers contrast brightly against the dark gray tones in the sky. It's beautiful, but it fills me with rage. I fight the urge not to grab those flowers, yank them off the bush, and stomp on them violently.

Life isn't supposed to be like this. I've supposed to be getting better, and in some ways, I have been. Ever since I found that book on the Epstein-Barr virus, I've spent the last eleven years learning about my health, observing my body, and figuring out what triggers the diarrhea and pain. It's been an exhausting journey of trial and error to find out what my body needs—and then stick to it and put my health first in a world where it's often easier to choose instant gratification over long-term wellbeing.

I'm in my thirties now. It's true that I no longer have diarrhea, full body pain, chronic fatigue, or daily nausea. I've made progress in many areas, but my dedication to a lifestyle that has improved my overall quality of life hasn't resolved any problems around my period. In fact, it's getting worse. The intolerable menstrual pain now lasts for days instead of hours, and I'm having these same excruciating pain flares away from my period —after having sex, after eating certain foods, and during bowel movements. The new gynecologist I saw yesterday—the third one I've seen in four months in my renewed quest to get a medical professional to take my symptoms seriously—suspects these symptoms are from endometriosis.

"This is a disease that gets worse over time," she said, recommending medically induced menopause or having a hysterectomy.[1] "Sometimes, you have to fight fire with fire."

These two recommendations are very serious, and I don't know what to do. It all makes me want to throw up. I abhor this awful disease called endometriosis. I'm infuriated that all that I've done for my health hasn't been enough to prevent me from being in this situation. As soon as I got home from that appointment, I searched online for holistic means to manage endometriosis symptoms, but everything I read told me to do exactly what I've been doing for the past eleven years! I am so frustrated and angry. Where do I go from here?

I stare at the innocent flower bush before me, enraged by its beauty. Why are these stupid pink flowers bothering me so much? I can imagine my meditation teacher's voice in my head, "Meditate on the flower." Whenever anything bothers me, she tells me to meditate on it. Well, I don't want to meditate on it! I just want it all to go away!

I feel trapped. I'm older now. I have more responsibilities, and life isn't as forgiving as it was in college. I can't just miss work every time I feel unwell, not like the way I used to miss class and make up the assignments. I'm afraid of how sick I'm getting, afraid of the consequences it might have on my ability to support myself economically. I'm pissed that all my hard work over the years hasn't paid off. At times, I've emotionally exhausted myself to always have food prepared that didn't make me sick, to make the time to exercise daily, to take ten day silent meditation retreats. I have spent all my free time learning about my body and my health and then putting those habits into place. So why am I still sick?!

I'm so angry I can barely breathe. I exhale loudly. "In and out, Amy; in and out." The air outside is cool and refreshing. As I focus on it coming in my lungs, I remind myself, "There you go with the black and white and no shades of gray." Yes, this situation is awful and infuriating, but it's not a fair assessment to say that my habits haven't paid off—because they *have*. My life has turned around from a decade ago. My lifestyle changes have enabled me to go from being unable to work to holding a full-time job. They have taken away my severe fatigue and filled me with energy. They have reduced my severe pain-days from thirty-one a month to roughly ten (although that's currently going up in number with these new flares I'm having). What I am doing has helped me improve my overall health, but it can't work miracles against an illness that has no cure.

I've done an excellent job of taking care of myself, but if the gynecologist is correct, I'm still sick because I have endometriosis. I have to wrap my head around that—I can't believe all this time I've had an undiagnosed disease! I want to vomit from the thought of it. I lean over and put my hands on my knees, breathing in deeply, trying to calm my stomach. I find my face just a few inches from those stupid flowers.

They stare calmly back at me, pink beauty piercing my soul and completely oblivious to my inner turmoil. I sigh loudly, then continue walking along the street. Being given a suspected diagnosis of an incurable disease is shocking. It's awful. It's sad. It's okay that I need time to process this. It's okay to have these emotions toward this beautiful flower bush—I'm not actually going to take my anger out on it. Yanking the flowers off and stomping on them are just thoughts. Still, I can't resist telling off the flower as I walk away. It's out of place; it's too gorgeous for this dreary day.

Self-Reflection

- Think of a time that you felt angry. What happened?
- Can you pinpoint exactly what made you angry?
- Did you feel like your anger was justified or that you had the right to feel angry?
- How does anger feel in your body? Is it hot, does it explode out of you, does your body tense, does your heart race, do your palms sweat?
- How do you normally deal with your anger? Do you repress it?
- Do you lash out when you are angry, do/say things that you later regret, or withdraw into yourself?
- If so, do you think the next time that you're angry you can try taking a deep breath and considering why exactly you're feeling angry and if there's anything you could do to help calm yourself down?

53

DESPERATION AND DESPAIR

A memory from college.

My diarrhea was so severe that I was afraid to leave my dorm room for fear of having an accident in public. I was constantly missing class because I was stuck in the fetal position in bed from pain. I felt completely disconnected from my friends who were living a carefree college lifestyle, I had quit every extracurricular activity, and I had rashes on my hips and butt from lying down so much.

I had just stumbled out of the bathroom after having diarrhea for the fifth time that hour. My troll doll watched me from her spot on the bed, her *Get well soon* dress taunting me with what felt like the fake hope of a dream that would never come true. "Stop staring at me!" I screamed at her. "Do something!"

In a fit of rage, I grabbed her and threw her across the room. She hit the wall and bounced onto the floor.

I fell to my knees, sobbing. All of those doctors and their tests, and no one could figure out what was wrong with me. It had been two years already. It was killing me not knowing why my whole body hurt all the time, why I was always so tired, why

I was always so sick. It was killing me not knowing if those desperate times would end. I felt like I didn't even know myself anymore.

After about twenty minutes, I managed to stop crying. I looked across the room and saw my dolly face down on the floor, one of her slippers hanging off her foot. "Oh my god!" I gasped and rushed over to her.

I rocked her in my arms as if she were a baby. "It's okay," I soothed her. "It's all going to be okay. I'm sorry I threw you like that. Please forgive me. You're okay. You're okay."

When would *I* be okay?

Self-Reflection

- For you, what has been the worst part about getting sick and why? For example, have you had to give up favorite activities? Is it the symptoms themselves or the way it has made you feel emotionally? Has being sick shaken your identity and the way you view yourself? Have the hard times brought out qualities in yourself that you don't like? Do you have difficulty getting through simple tasks? Has your illness affected your relationships?
- What do you feel thinking about this? Sad, angry, frustrated, confused, lost?
- How do you feel hearing the words "It'll be okay one day"?

54

THE WAY WE FACE OUR PROBLEMS

Many people say that the only thing we can control in life is how we face our problems. In theory, this makes sense. In actuality, the way I have reacted to my problems has seemed completely *out* of my control. Until recently, when things went wrong, I definitely wasn't acting in a way that I wanted to.

I feel ashamed of how I've acted most of my life. A few months ago, I ate something that upset my bladder and I ended up peeing on myself in front of my partner. I didn't want to burst into tears and then run away in embarrassment, but that's exactly what happened. I would have loved to have smiled calmly at him, laughed, and said, "Oops! I'll be right back. I'm going to change."

Or recently, when I completely lashed out at my mom. She had baked my favorite childhood cookies for me as a surprise. It was really sweet of her, but it infuriated me. I had told her that I was no longer eating cookies because they made me flare, but she had forgotten. When she offered them to me, I blew up, yelling that it was inconsiderate to bring something that made me sick and that I would have to say no to. I feel horrible at how upset I got—I was truly awful to her.

I abhor the way I tend to react to my problems, especially because I anger so easily. Afterwards, I am always filled with shame and self-loathing at how much of a rage I got into. Every time I hear people say that how we react to a situation is the only thing we truly control in life, I feel like a failure and disgusted with myself. If I were in control, I wouldn't act the way I do. I'm not choosing these reactions—they just happen.

But if I stop judging myself for my reactions, I can take a step back and see that like most of my thoughts, my reactions are subconscious patterns of behavior that I learned. They are responses programmed into my mind; they are habits that I immediately do without even thinking about them!

With this understanding, I'm working on breaking these automatic reactions and replacing them with the conscious actions of my choosing. It's tough work and slow going, as most change is in the beginning. Once more, it's vital to have self-compassion and be gentle with myself. From what I've read of the mind, many of my unwanted behavior patterns were learned before I was even seven years old! How can I judge myself for that? And judging my reactions, and therefore myself, as awful doesn't change anything—if it did, my reactions would have changed at least a little over the last fifteen years!

The word *Vipassana*, which is the type of meditation that I practice, comes from the Pali language and translates to *special seeing, insight, to see clearly*. How fitting because meditation has been teaching me how to observe my thoughts and see them how they are: without getting wrapped up in them, without judging them, and, most importantly, without believing them. Now I'm observing my reactions as well, practicing my skills at being a 'witness' to them. Slowly but surely my reactions are becoming less uncontrollable than they once were. I'm getting better at catching myself when I'm in the middle of a subconscious behavior pattern, just as I've been learning to notice when I'm swept away by a story my mind is telling. When I realize I'm reacting in a way I don't like, I pause. It's not easy, but I'm improving with practice.

Why pause? To notice and understand whatever I'm feeling. If I'm angry, I feel heat rising up in my body threatening to explode. It almost feels intolerable, expanding like it's trying to burst out of me. I notice how my hands are balled into fists; my body is tense. I force myself to close my eyes and focus on my breathing. As I inhale, I identify what I'm feeling: "Rage." I stand there a few minutes without moving, breathing heavy breaths. "Rage, rage, rage, rage."

When the anger fades, I move onto phase two of breaking my reactions: I 'get curious' about them. This is a tactic I've been using to see what's behind the unwanted thoughts, stories, and emotions in my life. I'm replacing *judging* them with *investigating* them, as if I were a detective to my psyche. Why did I become so angry? It's interesting to take this approach because sometimes what I discover really surprises me.

'Getting curious' with my emotions is leading to a better understanding of myself. It's revealed that what my anger often masks is fear. I'm full of insecurities and a deep-rooted fear that I am not good enough. Many times when I get angry I'm actually feeling frightened that somehow, due to the situation or my being sick, my loved ones will abandon me. Will they find me a burden or realize I'm truly unloveable? The same toxic subconscious stories seep their way into every aspect of my life.

I am grateful to have found the teachings of Vipassana and *seeing clearly.* I consider meditation strength training for my mind and even more important than the exercise I do daily for my physical body. After all, my mind is what completely interprets my reality! It's responsible for how I feel, respond, and exist in this world. My mind can lock me into an unwanted way of thinking and living, or my mind can be the key to emotional freedom. I want freedom. I don't want to react to situations in ways I'll later regret, hurt over and over again by subconscious thought and behavior patterns, so I'm striving to pause and analyze what I feel. I want to live my life the way I decide and no longer from unwanted subconscious conditioning!

I've been asking myself, "How do I want to respond to this situation? How do I want to feel about this?" These questions are empowering and full of possibility. By pausing to carefully reflect on them, I'm starting to create a different life for myself. My life is filled with circumstances that are uncontrollable—like endometriosis, period pain, and flares—but my relationship with these challenges is starting to finally be in my control. Although my outside circumstances are not changing, *I* am changing from the person that I *am* to the person I *want* to be.

Self-Reflection Prompt

- How do you react to your problems? Do you react the way you would like to?
- Without judging yourself, think about a situation where you didn't react the way you would have liked to. What happened? How did you react?
- What would you have liked to do differently? How do you wish you would have reacted?
- What could have helped you react that way? For example, would it have been helpful to pause and take a breath for a minute or ask more questions to better understand the situation?
- What feelings were present in your reaction? For example, were you angry or embarrassed?
- Explore if any fears may have been underneath that emotion—what do you think was at that feeling's core?

55

I SEE YOU SUFFERING

Endometriosis has been a heavy burden on my shoulders since I was seventeen years old, and many of us get sick at an even younger age—at twelve years old, at nine years old.

As I think about all that I have experienced—all that *we* with endometriosis have experienced—tears stream down my face. Moments of trauma and emotional pain flash before my eyes:

I see an eighteen-year-old alone in the doctor's office, sobbing in fear as the doctor tells her the colonoscopy found nothing. "Then what's wrong with me?!" she desperately asks him.

I see a twenty-year-old who fell to the ground on her busy college campus, vomiting in the grass in front of her peers.

I see a twenty-two-year-old hugging her troll doll as she twists and squirms on the bed, sobbing and thanking her doll profusely for being there with her, for not leaving her alone with this pain.

I see a twenty-four-year-old too fatigued to be a bridesmaid at her best friend's wedding and having to tell the bride the day before the wedding that she wasn't going to make it.

I see a twenty-five-year-old begging the doctor to do more

tests. He looks at her with raised eyebrows as she fights against his accusation: "It's not psychosomatic," she says, "I know there's something really wrong with me!"

I see a twenty-seven-year-old in incapacitating pain stumbling down a busy sidewalk, desperately trying to make it one more block back to her apartment.

I see a twenty-nine-year-old gripping her back while pacing frantically, begging out loud for the pain to stop.

I see her in all of her traumatic moments—dozens of them—and my heart breaks for her. I grieve for her fear, her loneliness, her desperation. I grieve for all that she has been through. Thinking about these moments, I can really see how hard things were and how tired her soul was.

She felt haunted by her pain, with little compassion and empathy from those around her, abandoned and neglected by a medical system that took sixteen years to diagnose her.

I take a deep breath to bring myself back to the present moment. These memories are overwhelming, and I just want to curl up in a quiet safe place. I decide to make myself into a ball in the corner of the closet, squished between the wall and an empty suitcase, beautiful dresses hanging over me that I never feel well enough to wear. I sit there in the darkness and allow myself to cry, loudly and unashamedly without holding back. "I see you suffering," I choke out between sobs. "I see you suffering, and I'm here with you."

Self-Reflection

Think of a time when you didn't feel seen or when you needed comfort but didn't receive any. For example, it could be a time when you weren't shown any empathy for your illness, when a doctor dismissed your symptoms, or when you had a difficult day due to a flare. What happened?

In your mind's eye, can you bring your present-self back to

be there alongside your past-self? Imagine present-you giving past-you what you needed back then. This might be a warm embrace, a listening ear, an acknowledgement of your pain. Tell past-you, "I see you. I'm here with you."

What other messages does past-you need to hear in that moment?

56

BE PROUD OF YOURSELF

When I measure myself to society's general idea of success, I feel like I'm failing.

For many, success in today's world is equated with finances and material possessions. Thanks to endometriosis, I haven't advanced in my career. There were years when my symptoms were too severe to work, and when I did enter the workforce, I was struggling just to keep my job. I currently rent a small apartment and live very frugally, as medical expenses eat into most of my salary.

Motherhood is often seen as a measurement of success for womxn in our society. I am thirty-three, not a mother, and due to reasons like infertility, economic instability, and the burdensome demands of taking care of myself, I may never be.

The societal definition of success is more about where our lives end up and what they look like on the outside rather than the person we have become. The focus isn't on our internal qualities such as our compassion, resilience, or grit. To me, that is real success: that we push through muck up to our necks, that we learn to swim when the flood begins, and that we continue to swim as the rain pours down. We never give up, even though we are exhausted.

How many times have we thought that we couldn't face a particular situation—but then we do? I think of the times when I have a flare at work and hide in the bathroom stall, muffling my sobs with my hands. *You can do this,* I tell myself, then exit the bathroom and continue my work. The times when I'm at the grocery store, nauseous and in pain, and I am so fatigued that I want to lie down on the floor in the middle of the baking aisle, and it takes every ounce of motivation in me to keep pushing the cart and go to the checkout line. *You can do this,* I tell myself, then I pay for my groceries and leave. The times when I see the blood on the toilet paper and realize that my period has arrived and those agonizing cramps are just a minute away. *You can do this,* I tell myself, then brace myself for what's to come. It's incredible to look back at what we've gotten through and see how strong we really are, especially when we felt anything *but* strong at the time.

Before I found my endometriosis specialist and finally got a diagnosis, I went to several gynecologists looking for help with my symptoms. One appointment stands out in my mind. I was thirty-one years old and had been sick for more than fourteen years at that point. I told the doctor that I was doing everything I could—following an anti-inflammatory diet, sleeping well, exercising and meditating daily—and yet my quality of life was still low due to my flares (although it was better than it had been before adopting these habits). I told her that I was losing hope and that I just couldn't understand why I was in such pain.

The doctor must have sensed the desperation in my voice. She put her hand on my shoulder, looked me in the eyes and said very gently, the way a parent may say to their child, "You are doing such a great job taking care of yourself. You should be extremely proud of the way you are handling what life has thrown at you."

As soon as she left the room, I started sobbing uncontrollably. I literally couldn't pull myself together. No one had ever said that to me before, and it moved me deeply. Although she didn't know how to diagnose or help my physical symptoms, her kindness and compassion served that day as medicine for my soul. Her words have stuck with me through my scariest moments—my two surgeries, my grapefruit-sized endometrioma and cancer scare, countless episodes of debilitating pain, and a recent new health diagnosis.

We are dealing with really hard situations and symptoms that many people just don't understand. We are doing an incredible job living with this devastating illness called endometriosis—even on the days when it doesn't feel like enough, even on the days when we feel like we could do better.

Our success is immeasurable and we should, beyond a shadow of a doubt, feel proud of ourselves.

Self-Reflection

- How do you feel toward yourself with all that you've been through?
- Do you feel proud of yourself for the effort you've put in to take care of yourself or for your ability to get through the challenging moments?
- If you are having trouble feeling proud or are instead finding a lot of guilt or self-criticism, can you recall a time when you felt you did well with something? For example, you handed in your work project on time, prepared dinner for yourself instead of ordering takeout like you had wanted to, or gave yourself a few moments of self-care.
- How do you define success?
- We all have been successful in something. Using your

definition and not anyone else's, in what ways have you been successful in your life? For example, learning to manage your symptoms, always managing to get out of bed in the morning, taking a walk daily to help with your pain.

57

I WON'T LIVE IN FEAR ANYMORE

It always takes several days to recover from my period and for the colors of the world to brighten once again. As the pain fades, so do the images in my mind of myself thrashing frantically in pain on the floor. But how can I truly let go when the memory is scheduled to become reality again? Just three weeks later, I'll relive this same nightmare.

How do you get over something that keeps coming back? The pain is haunting me; it's a gaping wound that never gets the chance to heal, a ghost that walks by my side at all times. Each month, the imprint of the trauma it leaves on my soul grows.

This month's torture is on the horizon—my period is coming in a day or two. I feel a knot in my stomach. It's three a.m.—a dark hour. I am awake and alone. I get in the shower to chase away the cold fear in my bones. Leaning on the wall of the shower, I scrub myself desperately, hoping it will wash away the sickness. *Go down the drain.* They are showers to cleanse my soul.

As I get back in bed, warm and clean, I remind myself of my teachings. "Be in the moment," I tell myself. "You are safe right now. Feel the softness of the covers against your skin. Feel your breath rise and fall in your chest." I try to do so, but my mind keeps hijacking the moment, repeatedly bringing up an image of me clutching my back in agony, a posture I spend hours in during my period. The knot in my stomach hardens.

For over a decade, I've been living in a constant state of fear. Day in and day out, attending to my basic human needs—eating, peeing, and pooping—causes brutal flares. I'm terrified of food, traveling, sneezing, bending down, speed bumps, drinking water, and anything and everything that might cause me a spontaneous pain flare. I have completely lost any feeling of safety within my body. Living means constantly walking on eggshells because any minute, the most 'normal' thing could trigger a flare.

Lying here, with tears in my eyes and overwhelmed by the fear of my future pain, I bring forward a commitment I recently made to myself: I won't live in fear anymore. As I continue learning about the neuroscience behind thought patterns, behavioral reactions, and mindset, I'm discovering that I can also learn to calm my fear response.

What is fear, anyway? It's emotion and a survival mechanism; it's the way the mind attempts to alert us to danger to help keep us safe. Some fears are innate, but most fears—like mine of my period—are learned. Lying here in the quiet of the night, paying attention to my body and breathing deeply, I acknowledge that fear is present with me. But I am not my fear, and this is an important distinction: I'm experiencing fear, but *I* am not fear. My shoulders are tense, my breath is shallow, and my stomach is hardened, but I am not fear. This is just what fear feels like in my body. Everyone in the world has felt fear in their own bodies at some point or another.

I stand up from the bed to do a movement from Qigong, a centuries-old wellness practice that coordinates slow standing movements with the breath. It's often used for health, healing, and martial arts training, with potential benefits like increasing energy, relieving stress and anxiety, and stretching the body. I find it helpful to do when I'm overpowered by fear. The slow movements combined with the deep breathing calm my heightened nervous system, and the act of doing something helps me feel more in control.

I bend down and make a motion with my hands like I'm scooping something up from the ground. I imagine myself gathering energy from the earth. I visualize it as a golden color, and I raise it to chest level. Then I use my hands to shape it into a ball and bathe myself in it, miming the motion of splashing water on my face.

I repeat this flowing movement several times until I feel calmer. Then I lie down again, close my eyes, and do an imagery meditation that also involves light. This time, I imagine the light inside of my heart—as love. It, too, is a golden color, and as I sit here breathing slowly and focusing on its radiance, I begin to feel its warmth in my chest. As I visualize it engulfing me, I imagine the edges of my body melting into the light. It is a powerful healing force that is helping tear down the walls I constructed around my heart long ago to protect myself.

Exercises like these used to feel ridiculous to me, but now I find myself turning to them often. In moments of crisis, a few minutes of Qigong or image visualization—or both—can soothe my fear and anxiety, completely changing the mindset I find myself in. My fear feels so much bigger than me, but scooping up energy from the earth or accessing the love inside of me brings in forces that are bigger than my fear. This makes space for the fear, which helps me feel like I can breathe again.

I am learning to untie the knot of fear in my stomach that is triggered in me by everyday activities and the anticipation of the pain.[1] The more I slowly begin to sit with the fear that comes up around my pain, the more I see that, little by little, I can be with it. Just as the ocean is vast and can hold its enormous storms, I, too, can hold the full magnitude of my fear—as well as other overwhelming emotions such as my anger, shame, and grief. I thought these feelings in all their rawness would consume me, but the opposite is happening—the more I slowly let them in, the less hold they have over me and the freer I become.

Self-Reflection

- Have you built an emotional wall around your heart or somehow closed your heart off?
- How do you know that you have or you haven't?
- If you have closed off your heart, why did you do that?
- When did you do that? Was there a certain moment, or did it happen gradually over time?
- Do you want to open your heart or tear down the wall?
- If so, what do you think can help you with that?
- If not, why do you want to keep the walls up?
- If you don't have an emotional wall around your heart, why do you think people build them around theirs?
- Why did you never feel the need to build one around yours?

58

I EMBRACE THIS LIFE AS IT IS

I often ask myself the question: What kind of life do I want?

One full of peace. I really want peace. All the never ending doctor's appointments that have to be juggled with a full-time job, the years of rushing hourly to the bathroom, a decade and a half of debilitating menstruation—I want peace. My life is intertwined with endometriosis, and I don't see that changing. Peace is not going to come find me. If I want peace, then I need to actively *make* peace with my life.

How infuriated I once felt at the idea of accepting stabbing vagina pains, bowel movements that make me cry out in agony, and fatigue that has me literally passing out at times. I was sure that I could never be okay with any of that. My anger and grief made sense given how devastating those symptoms are—these emotions are valid and perfectly natural. But after a decade of living *from* these emotions, I've only found myself drained and broken. There's been no joy in my life, no meaning, no happiness. There's only been hatred and fear. Is this the kind of life I want?

Learning to shift toward neutrality, learning that I *could* shift to neutrality—this has opened up such freedom in the way I feel. Moving toward living a life where peace and acceptance is at the forefront, rather than fear and hatred, is a big shift. Accepting that endometriosis is part of my life won't ever make my pain any less intense, but it would mean not living in this perpetual and detrimental fight-or-flight mode.

Like life, endometriosis has many layers, and I've found peace with some of them. It no longer bothers me to follow an anti-inflammatory diet or cook all my own food. It took several years of fighting against it and hating it fervently—cooking takes so much time and effort—but I have finally embraced this change. Surprisingly (I really felt this would never be the case), I no longer miss the foods I cut out or feel deprived, restricted, or sad when I pass by the cheese, cookies, or bread in the grocery store. In fact, I actually feel happy that, by eating the way I do, I can reduce my pain and fatigue.

There are other aspects of endometriosis, like painful sex, that I haven't fully accepted. But in the process of *finding* peace, in the searching and looking for peace, I've been able to turn down the volume of how much painful sex hurts me emotionally. It used to crush my heart that something that I want to share with a partner is off the table right now. But now, I feel more neutral about it—it just slightly pulls on my heart. On a 1-10 scale, the emotional stress has gone from a 10 to a 5. Will I ever get to a 0? Will I ever have full peace or neutrality? I don't know. But pressuring myself to feel a certain way won't help me feel that way. Where I'm at, even if it's a 10, is okay. I'm just being where I am now. Acceptance is a process that takes time, and even going from completely emotionally shattered to somewhat less shattered has already improved my life. I feel less broken and more whole; I am calmer and more collected when I talk about painful sex and look for other ways to share intimacy.

I certainly won't ever be happy that I have endometriosis,

but getting to neutral—accepting the pain, the fear, and the life changes I've needed to make—is much less exhausting than fighting against it and rejecting it. I realized that rejecting endometriosis means rejecting a part of myself.

In the exact moment of writing those words, I get a stabbing pain in my abdomen. Part of me wants to say that my endometriosis is taunting me. "Be at peace with this!" it screams out.

In the past, I might have interpreted this sudden pain as a reminder that I will never feel better or that making peace with my illness is an idealistic impossibility. But today something different comes up inside me—I begin to laugh and talk to the pain. It feels empowering to address this stupid disease and tell it my new goal. "Oh, endometriosis, I know your tricks. Sorry to disappoint you, but you no longer get to decide how I feel about my life and these things that happen to me."

The pain holds steady, but so do I. "Endo, you aren't in charge of whether or not I have joy, frustration, or sadness. You don't get to decide my happiness. Not anymore. *Only I do.*"

My abdomen stabs me again in what feels like a desperate attempt to show me who is really in charge of my emotions. I take a few slow, deep breaths as the pain intensifies. "Go ahead! Bring on the pain, bring on the nausea, bring on the fatigue! Give me your worst!" I challenge it. "I'm learning how to be okay no matter what you do."

Pacing usually helps me with this kind of pain, so I pull myself up and step outside onto the porch, both hands pressing on the spot on my abdomen where the pain is screaming. I look up at the sky; the beautiful, expansive, open sky. It's a deep gray and filled with ominous looking clouds. It's clearly going to rain any minute. There is a strong, cool breeze which chills me slightly.

I tell my disease again in a calm, confident voice, "You're not in charge of how I feel. Only *I* will decide how I feel."

I imagine that the wind picks up my words and carries them down the street, giving weight to my message, spreading it as a fact I will try my best to hold to. I speak a little louder. "Only I will decide how I feel!" The wind bundles up my message and carries it around the neighborhood. "Only I will decide how I feel!" Off goes my truth around the city. I take a deep breath and scream out as loud as I can, "Do you hear me, endometriosis? Only I will decide how I feel!"

Self-Reflection

- Do you think it's possible to turn down the volume of how much something hurts you emotionally?
- Are there any aspects of your illness that you feel more neutral toward (and for example, less sad or less angry toward) than you once did? Have you been able to turn down the volume of how much this aspect hurts you mentally or emotionally? For example, did it used to be a 10 out of 10 but now has dropped to a 9 or even less?
- Think about an aspect of endometriosis that you would like to feel more neutral toward. What benefits would it bring you to feel more neutral about it? For example, would you feel more whole, or calmer, or like a weight was lifted from your chest?

59

LAYERS OF HEALING

There is no cure for endometriosis, but that doesn't mean I can't heal. I'm not referring to my body but rather all that isn't physical: the broken trust I have in myself, the walls I've constructed around my heart, the resentments I carry.

As I examine different aspects of my life and especially the inner layers of myself, I'm starting to think that acceptance goes hand in hand with healing emotionally.

What does acceptance mean to me? To keep an open heart to circumstances as they are, to stop needing my life to be different in order to be at peace.

What does healing mean to me? To be at peace, to live from love, to be connected to the world, to be whole.

The wording is slightly different, but the end feeling of peace, wholeheartedness, and love is the same. By accepting endometriosis, I am healing both spiritually and emotionally. Through healing, it's becoming easier to accept my circumstances and my life as it is. Both processes are pushing me to bring loving awareness to parts of me that I have pushed away, buried, or have operating on an autopilot from habits I unknowingly made decades ago.

Why is this important? Because the relationship I have with my endometriosis has been conditioned by a complex web of all the various parts of me:

my self-confidence
my expectations of life
my relationships with loved ones, food, and work
my ability to set boundaries, to manage stress, and to process emotions
the people I surround myself with, both the toxic and supportive ones
what I assign value to
where I derive my self-worth
my beliefs
my priorities.

The further I investigate the depths of myself, the more the paths of both acceptance and healing unfold before me, inviting in a new way to experience life.

Self-Reflection

- What does healing mean to you?
- For you, what relationship is there between acceptance and healing?
- What has your relationship with endometriosis been conditioned by?
- What parts of your life have you buried, pushed away, or ignored that need your loving attention?

60

MY PAIN WAS ALWAYS REAL

It's been eight months since receiving a suspected diagnosis of endometriosis (after over sixteen years of being sick). During these last months, I've been learning as much as I can about the disease. It hasn't been easy considering all the misinformation out there, and it took me a few months to even learn that this is a major issue with endometriosis! After finally finding credible sources of information written by excision experts and well-informed patient advocates,[1] I became aware that everything I had learned previously was actually incorrect. While a hysterectomy may indeed have a place in some patients' care (each case to be discussed individually between the patient and their doctor), it is a myth that a hysterectomy cures endometriosis. As for the medical menopause treatment my doctor offered me, it is *symptom* management only and cannot remove the disease itself. Additionally, I learned that even if it did help my pain, it's only a temporary fix; there is a limit to how long I could be on this medication due to the risk of serious side effects. As for ablation surgery, it superficially burns the surface of the endometriosis, which can result in endometriosis persisting since it wasn't completely removed.

Symptoms and pain often return quite quickly after this surgery. However, there is a technique called excision surgery that can remove the disease at the root. This is considered 'the gold standard' of endometriosis care.

What I learned from my research was that my current doctor does not have the knowledge or experience necessary with endometriosis to provide me 'the gold standard' of care, but there are doctors who specialize in endometriosis who can. Unfortunately, it's estimated that there are less than 200 endometriosis excision specialists worldwide. This is such a tiny number considering the millions of us with this disease!

By some stroke of incredible luck and fortune, I found an excision surgery in my city, and he even took my insurance. The earliest appointment he had available was a few months later. After setting the date and hanging up with the receptionist, I started crying from relief and happiness. Was this really happening? I was elated to have this privilege to receive what's considered 'the gold standard' for treatment. I had a glimmer of hope that I might finally get relief from my pain, but at the same time, I also felt incredibly doubtful. No tests or doctor had ever found anything wrong—what if this surgeon didn't find anything either?

At my initial appointment with the surgeon, I told him my long list of symptoms. He listened attentively and kindly and then said, "Many of my patients have pain like yours. Chances are very high that it's endometriosis." It was so beautiful not to have to try and convince him to take my pain seriously, like I had to do with so many previous doctors. I was extremely impressed by him and excited at the idea that having him as my doctor might actually lead to me feeling better. At the same time, I tried not to get my hopes up too much—what if the surgery still found nothing? Or what if it did and after excision I still didn't feel better?

We scheduled surgery in two months. I returned to his office a few weeks after this initial visit for the preoperative ultrasound. I was excited but nervous, certain I was going to leave disappointed. Endometriosis is not usually seen via ultrasound, and the one I had eight months earlier with my previous gynecologist had been 'normal'.

There was a big screen up on the wall so I could see exactly what the doctor saw. To my shock, the ultrasound showed that I had a giant mass measuring twelve centimeters across, eight wide, and five long. It was bigger than my fist. The doctor also pointed out at least three pockets of fluid and that my uterus appeared rotated. "We are probably looking at stage IV endometriosis with bowel involvement," he said, "and we will have to remove your left ovary due to the mass."

WHAT?!

This was what I had wanted since I was seventeen years old. To be believed. To be validated. To finally know what was causing pain so severe it made me vomit and shake.

I have endometriosis. A monster of a disease. No cure.

I just couldn't believe it.

I left in a daze, completely shocked. While my previous gynecologist had said I likely had endometriosis, I hadn't actually conceptualized what this meant or how severe the damage could be until seeing it on the screen during that ultrasound. It was all suddenly so real, and it hit me like a ton of bricks. Suddenly, my body felt so heavy. The thought of losing my ovary or having a bowel resection terrified me.

I sat in my car in the hospital parking lot, too upset to drive. My blood started to boil; I could feel a deep rage rising up from inside of me. I imagined myself holding a baseball bat and just beating it against the side of the car, as hard as I could, smashing the mirror to bits, breaking the window, denting the doors. In my mind, I pounded that bat against my car with all my might, screaming in fury.

Flashbacks came to my mind of the sixteen years of doubt and dismissal I faced from those around me. Countless doctors had told me that the pain was from anxiety! They had embarrassed me, discrediting me in front of loved ones who came with me to the appointments, telling me that I couldn't have menstrual pain that intense and "Some women just can't handle pain." They all accused me, "You're crying wolf!" But the wolf had always been real, devouring me slowly over years, haunting me with pain, devastating my life. No one had realized I had endometriosis, let alone treated it, and because of that it had progressed to stage IV and now I was going to lose an ovary.

Not to mention all that I had emotionally suffered over the years without an official medical justification for my pain and bowel problems. How much it affected me psychologically to have no explanation to give friends, teachers, and bosses for my absences, body's unreliability, and frequent need for the toilet. They wanted to know why I was doubled over in pain again, why I was so fatigued again, why I had to cancel plans again—but I had no idea why.

That led to the assumptions, which made me doubt myself and the pain I was experiencing:

"You're just lazy," partners said. "You just don't want to get out of bed."

"It can't hurt as badly as you say it does," friends said.

"Stop exaggerating," teachers said.

"What have you done wrong? It seems like you are being punished by God."

"You probably did something in a past life to deserve this."

"The pain is in your head."

"Maybe you're not meant to survive because evolution always favors the strong and you are clearly weak."

"Medically unexplained symptoms are often psychosomatic."

"You're overly sensitive."

"Don't be so dramatic."

"I've never seen anyone in pain like you. Are you just looking for attention?"

It's hard to find the strength to face something unbearable when everyone is telling you that what you are going through isn't even real. That day, it was proven real. Sitting there in my car fuming after that ultrasound, it felt like someone had finally opened a window and after sixteen years I was no longer gasping for air.

It wasn't *ever* in my head.

My pain was always *real.*

Getting diagnosed, while extremely validating, didn't immediately undo all the psychological damage that had been done in those years of having little support. Sixteen years is a long time to hear cruel, dismissive comments that chip away at your self-worth.

Unknowingly, I had internalized those uninvited comments, coming to my own subconscious conclusion about why I was sick: because I was inadequate. After all, almost two dozen doctors—in the United States and Japan—couldn't find anything physically wrong with me. Nothing I did helped the pain, either. It was obvious that there was something *inherently* wrong with me as a person, and that's why I was sick. I must be deeply flawed, neurotic, and to blame for my symptoms.

This was reinforced with how my efforts to help my symptoms didn't eliminate them. Over the years, I committed to almost every health practice that I came across: diet change, lifestyle modification, mind-body medicine, journaling, reading self-help books, going on meditation retreats. Some worked for me, some didn't. As I figured out what my body needed, I gained more energy and my diarrhea diminished, but to my disappointment, the episodes of intolerable pain slowly grew longer and more frequent. And I couldn't understand why. In articles online and on podcasts, people raved about they cured their pain by journaling about repressed emotions, cutting out gluten, prioritizing sleep, taking fish oil, managing their stress, and all sorts of therapeutic and healthy activities that I was devoting myself wholeheartedly to. But while some of my symptoms—the fatigue, some of the flares associated with eating—improved, my pain, especially around my period, only *worsened.*

Of course, I hadn't known that I was sick because I had endometriosis, let alone how serious endometriosis is and that it can cause organs to fuse together, bowel blockages, digestive problems, high levels of chronic inflammation, or an upregulation of the central nervous system. I couldn't have known that diet, lifestyle, and mindset couldn't cure me nor that I would need excision surgery to remove the disease from my body.

What I had known was that I had been told over and over that my bloodwork, scans, and test results were 'perfect'. And my perfect body was extremely sick and no matter what I did, it failed to improve my health.

Obviously, it was *my* fault. Obviously, I didn't deserve to feel better. Obviously, it was some kind of punishment for the person that I was. If not, then why couldn't I handle my pain, which supposedly was normal? Why did no one else I knew have a period like I did? Why, no matter how hard I tried, didn't I feel better?

As I sat in my car in the parking lot, stunned by the results of the ultrasound, I realized that the answers I had invented to those questions were not the true answers at all. The cause of my health problems was not my inadequacy as a person; it was not because I was broken, too sensitive, or weak.

I had been sick, fatigued, and in pain all these years because I had an undiagnosed, serious illness called endometriosis—the cause of which is not my fault. Getting diagnosed solved the mystery that had been hanging over my health for more than half of my life; it lightened the heavy load that had been pressing on my shoulders all of that time.

I sobbed in my parked car for over an hour before managing to drive home, tears still streaming down my face. They were of grief for all that my younger self had endured because maybe if I had gotten treated sooner my endometriosis wouldn't have advanced to stage IV; of rage for the countless people, especially doctors, who brushed off my symptoms; and of joy because I didn't realize how beautiful and liberating it would be to get an explanation as to why I was so sick—a reason that didn't involve me being inherently broken.

Self-Reflection

- How long did it take you to be diagnosed?
- How did you feel when you were diagnosed?
- What was your journey to diagnosis like? Did you face dismissal and disbelief from loved ones or doctors?
- Did people make uninvited comments to you? What did they say?
- Did you internalize these comments and make them truths about yourself?
- Do you see their unwanted comments reflected in the way you think about yourself now? If so, how?
- Can you tell yourself that this disease isn't your fault, and that you aren't broken or weak?

61

WATCHING MYSELF FROM AFAR

As I lie in bed, heating pad on my abdomen, resting from a flare, I recall what happened to me last week in a Vietnamese restaurant. Eyes closed, I see the situation play out before me, but it was like I was watching someone else. I watch a young woman emerge from the restroom, walking carefully and methodically back to the table where she was eating. Her breath was as slow as her footsteps. It almost looked as if she wasn't moving at all. Because of her slow pace, people began staring at her, but she just continued to look straight at the door, advancing forward one tiny step at a time.

When her partner saw her, he threw twenty dollars on the table and rushed over to meet her, to stand strong with her against the prying eyes. He gently slipped her arms into her jacket sleeves, careful not to jolt her body. He understood that at this moment she was holding back the beast.

She fumbled at the zipper. It was chilly out, but she was shaking from the pain, and her unsteady hands were unable to close the zipper. "I'll do it," her partner said gently. Every ounce of her willpower was concentrating on stepping forward without collapsing and making a scene. They made it out the door, and he rushed to get the car and pull it up to her in front of the restaurant.

He helped her into the passenger side and her body sagged against the reclined seat. "It hurts," she moaned, the cascade of tears falling now that she was safe from the morbid curiosity of strangers. Her face crumpled in pain. She closed her eyes. "I made it," she whispered.

"Yes, you did," his voice choked a little. She opened her eyes slowly and outstretched her hand to rest on his. Everything she did was in slow motion. "What's wrong?" She spoke faintly, and he could barely hear her.

"It breaks my heart to see you suffer."

The pressure tightened on his hand for a second, and he knew she was trying to squeeze it. "I know," she said. "It's unnerving the first few times. I have lived through this pain dozens of times. Alone," she said, her voice breaking from emotion. "I'm happy you are here with me."

She closed her eyes again and lay there with her hands pressing on her abdomen, waiting to arrive home to her bed.

I remember that day. I remember so many days; countless times when I watched that girl in those incredible moments of pain. How did I make it through them? It astounds me what we live through with this disease.

Self-Reflection

Recall a memory in which you were in pain, at a difficult doctor's appointment, had nausea, or with another struggle regarding your illness. Write a short story about yourself, but use **third person pronouns** as I did above, as if you were seeing yourself and the situation from the outside.

For example, *she was/he was/they were in the waiting room of the doctor's office with a sad look on her/his/their face. She/he/they picked up her/his/their purse...*

Now, re-read your story. Can you find the points where you surprised yourself? Where you made it through something because you had to? Where you stood up for yourself or simply made it out the other side okay? Take a moment to recognize how strong you are for what you go through.

62

THE LOSS OF IDENTITY

As I rushed into the bathroom to have diarrhea for the eighth time that hour, I glimpsed a woman in the mirror, her face beet red and crumpled up from sobbing, snot dripping down her face, a bit of puke on her chin. Her hair was a disheveled mess from rolling around on the floor in pain. Her clothes were drenched in sweat. Who was that staring back at me? Why did she look so hollow, lifeless, and broken? She looked like a shell of a person, and it scared me.

For years after getting sick, I didn't know myself anymore. My identity was completely shattered. I had to quit the activities I loved, and with that, I lost a vital part of me. I had spent the first sixteen years of my life figuring out who I am and what I like to do. When I was on the tennis court or in the karate dojo, I felt alive and life had meaning.

Then this was stolen from me by the fatigue, nausea, and pain. Suddenly, I found myself transplanted into a new reality of not feeling well, lying in bed, and sitting frequently on the toilet. When I went to college, I brought my tennis racket with me in hopes that I could play once in a while, but the few times I got on the court, I had to stop after hitting just a couple of balls—I was already exhausted. Whenever I would see my tennis racket in the corner of my dorm room closet, my breath would catch in my throat and I would be pinned down by sadness. The grief for all I had lost was crushing in the first few years. Almost every day, I fervently wished that I could revert back to my old self, the person I was before endometriosis symptoms swallowed up my life.

But there was no going back. More than a decade has passed since then. My tennis racket continues to be in the corner of the closet, but I've managed to play a few times over the years. When I catch a glimpse of my racket, I feel a twinge of nostalgia, but it's no longer a source of sorrow nor a symbol of a life I have lost. My memories of playing tennis now bring a smile instead of tears. I think about how I started playing when I was five years old, out on the court with my grandma, father, and sister. I recall the hot summers I spent down at the local recreation center on the red clay courts and the friends I had from these summer day camps. I'm able to cherish these memories, instead of being saddened and angered by them. I wasn't able to appreciate them ten years ago, five years ago, even two years ago, but enough time has passed that I'm now able to do so.

Time has helped me adapt. Time has allowed me to discover new activities, new goals and priorities, and new sources of meaning that are compatible with this new life of mine—a life that includes endometriosis. Although I no longer play tennis, I've found different ways to bring into my life the same feelings that tennis brought me: freedom, exhilaration, flow, concentration, time with loved ones.

Time has shown me that my identity is not fixed. Rather, it's flexible, changing with me throughout my lifetime. I've learned to stop looking backward and instead to look forward. They say that endings are really just new beginnings in disguise. Now that I have distance, I can say that this was true for me. Sixteen years ago, endometriosis came in and wrecked my life, but that forced me down a path of discovery. While I desperately wanted the doctors to fix me so that I could go back to my old life, I was learning to be empowered and make better decisions and commitments to take care of myself. Endometriosis ended the life I had, but it also began a new life with a new me.

It's been a bumpy ride since then, both ugly and beautiful, both exhausting and exhilarating. The loss of any identities has led to the finding of others, and in picking up the pieces, I've figured out the most important part—who I am underneath it all. Beyond the beliefs of 'tennis player,' 'athlete,' 'teacher,' 'aspiring mother,' 'sick,' and so many other labels I put on myself, I've realized that my true essence runs much deeper. In changing the question I focus on from, *What have I lost?* to *Who am I?* I've discovered the timeless qualities that have always been within myself.

I remember sitting at the welcome orientation for my first ten-day silent Vipassana retreat. They asked me to fill out a little information about myself, including the prompt, "Describe yourself." The blank page before me was waiting for me to fill it up with words. What did I want to say about myself? Had I never gotten sick, I probably would have written that I was a thirty-three-year-old woman who teaches English, plays tennis, and likes being outside. But instead, I thought for a minute about how I write my own story, both on this page before me and in life.

I picked up the pen and wrote:

I'm Amy. I have endometriosis, and this colors every aspect of my life. I make up for the days of pain by creating beauty with art and trying to put the same kindness out into the world that I have been lucky to receive. I hope that my empathy and compassion inspire others to find these same qualities inside themselves. I've learned that I am part of the eternal: of the stars, of the forests, of the love that drives this world forward. I do all that I can to try and live with this disease, and I've never given up.

That's the truth of who I am underneath it all: love, kindness, creativity, awareness, compassion, determination, resilience. It was only once the outward identity I had been building for years shattered to its core that I was able to find my true inner self.

Self-reflection

- What happened to your identity when you got sick? Did it shatter, or did you lose pieces of yourself?
- Did you have to quit any activities that you loved?
- Did/Do you dwell on the person that you used to be before getting sick or wish your life would go back to 'normal'?
- How have you been adapting since you first got sick?
- Have you found new activities that bring the same feelings into your life as any activities that you had to quit?
- Do you think that identity is flexible and changing?
- Can you think of any times that were an ending but also became a beginning?

63

IMMERSING MY PAIN IN LOVE

This is a moment of excruciating pain.

How long will this moment be? Will this pain ever fade? I breathe through my rising feelings of desperation and panic. "It's okay," I soothe myself. "This pain will end."

This is a moment of pain, but it's neither good nor bad. It just is, and I can expect nothing more and nothing less from life right now. My fate, at this moment, is to feel this pain. It's hard to be okay with that, but that's all I have right now. I don't have the ability to take the pain away or change this situation, but I *do* have the choice of whether or not to try and be okay with it.

"Let go," I tell my mind. Let go of judgments. Let go of thinking that it's an ugly fate, a terrible fate, an unjust fate. Let go of hating the pain and hating endometriosis. Let go of the self-pity and sadness about having to go through this. Let go of thinking that I deserve this—that is me projecting my own guilt and self-hatred onto my pain. The pain is not a punishment; it's just another experience among the millions of experiences of life. It's not even *my* pain; it's just *the* pain, nothing more. Let it be.

Beyond just trying to not judge the pain, I've recently been doing something new: sending love to it. The first time I heard this suggestion, I misunderstood what it meant. I thought that it meant I should love my pain, and that seemed sadistic to me. But the idea isn't to love my pain but to send love *to* it. This is much different than what I normally do, which is to reject the pain, hate it, and curse it—and in the process reject, hate, and curse *myself and my body* for having this pain.

I imagine waves of love washing over me; I envision myself being bathed with warm golden light. To send love to pain so monstrous that it steals the air from the room is a practice that I have worked up to. A few years ago, I began to practice this daily with a loving-kindness meditation. It was a guided meditation that instructed me to imagine sending love, kindness, and general good feelings to someone I loved. After a few weeks, I could actually visualize myself sending those feelings to an image of my loved one. In my mind's eye, I could see and even feel a warm golden light shining out of my heart into the world around me, the way the sun shines into space.

I then moved onto the next instruction: to send these feelings to someone neutral. I decided on the person who delivers the mail. I sometimes saw him when I looked out the window, but I didn't even know his name. For a few weeks I practiced, sitting quietly on my meditation cushion and imagining this light radiating out of my heart to a vision of him in my mind. It was weird at first and much harder to send these feelings to a stranger. Like all things, though, the more I practiced, the easier it became. I started with simply kindness and general good feelings—I tried to 'send' him best wishes for the rest of his day; I sent hope for peace, safety, and happiness in his life. Once I could do that, I started to try and include love—not a romantic love but a general feeling of caring and compassion, welcoming him into the world. Loving-kindness is simply, "You exist in this world; I see you, I accept and appreciate that you are here, and I wish you well."

The last instruction was to send loving-kindness out to someone that I disliked. I chose someone I didn't see often but who really got under my skin. This person hadn't done anything to me; she was just someone I generally found to be annoying. When I first brought up her image in my mind, I couldn't help but sigh loudly or roll my eyes. I felt ridiculous trying to send her love; it also seemed impossible to send love to someone who brought up such frustration in me. But after trying for several meditation sessions, my internal attitude softened toward her. Eventually, I was able to see her as a fellow human being that was also worthy of love and kindness. The first day that I managed to send her the simple best wishes that I easily sent to the person who delivers my mail, I felt so accomplished and proud of myself. From there on out, it got easier to send her feelings of acceptance and welcoming for her existence in this world.

It is a powerful experience to send love out of my heart. It's helping me strengthen my compassion and connection to others—even though they have no idea they are the focus of my loving-kindness practice. Through this practice, I'm starting to identify and take down walls I had built years ago around my heart. Unknowingly, I put them up to separate and protect myself from being hurt by others, but I don't want them there anymore.

Every day, I send loving-kindness out into the world for five minutes before bed. It's a seemingly insignificant practice that takes very little time or energy, but it has been a life-changing tool in the same way finding three reasons daily for gratitude has been: it's helping me experience the world from a place of fuller awareness and deeper happiness. I'm now even able to genuinely send loving-kindness to someone that I never expected I could—to myself in a moment of pain.

Enveloping my pain in love creates more space for the pain and more air in the room for me to breathe. I once scorned and belittled the idea of surrounding my pain with love, but now that I am able to do so, I can honestly say that it's helped me immensely during many terrifying and brutal moments of my life. On the contrary, no amount of anger ever loosened the pain's grasp on me; no amount of self-pity ever made the pain pass by faster. The countless times I asked, "Why me?" never helped. Begging and bargaining with the universe proved useless as well. All these tactics only made the pain feel even more unendurable.

But wrapping myself and my pain in loving-kindness helps me bear the intolerable. My pain has always felt so powerful and all-consuming, but my love is even more powerful than the pain. The light I imagine radiating from my heart—my love—is stronger than the pain radiating out of my abdomen. Although the physical pain doesn't diminish, the emotional pain of having to live through something so brutal does, and this has been incredibly healing to my soul.

Self-Reflection

- How does the idea of sending loving-kindness to your pain sound to you? For example, impossible, ridiculous, beautiful?
- What do you imagine when you think of sending love to your pain?
- Have you ever tried loving-kindness meditation? What was your experience with it?

Let's do loving-kindness meditation together right now. Sit or lie down in whatever posture is comfortable for you. Now imagine that a person or an animal that you love is sitting next to you. Visual sending them loving-kindness in your mind's eye. You might imagine this as an expanding ball of light, as warmth, as beams of love, as a beautiful feeling—there is no right or wrong way to imagine this.

Do this for at least three minutes. If you find that you have become lost in thoughts and stopped sending loving-kindness, that's okay. Just bring your attention back to the imaginary person or animal at your side, and resume sending them these feelings.

Now, take that same loving-kindness that you are sending to your loved one and direct it to your abdomen or an area where you frequently experience pain. Immerse this area in loving-kindness. Do this for three minutes.

- How easy or hard was it to send loving-kindness to your loved one?
- What about to the area of your pain?
- How did you imagine your love? Was it a certain color, temperature, or shape?
- Did the intensity/color/strength change when you sent it to your loved one versus when you sent it to your abdomen? If so, why do you think that is?

64

THE SHOCKING NEWS

Ten a.m. on a Friday. I was at work when the doctor's office called me. A week earlier, I had the pre-op ultrasound with the excision surgeon that revealed a mass twelve centimeters across—the width of a grapefruit—on my left ovary, along with various pockets of fluid. While looking at the scans, the doctor had said that it was most likely stage IV endometriosis.

When I answered the phone, the nurse introduced herself and jumped right into it: "In reference to your ultrasound last week, has anyone talked to you about the possibility of the mass being cancer?"

At the sound of the C word, my breath got stuck in my throat. The room started spinning, and I rushed into my best friend's office, putting the phone on speakerphone. She looked up from her computer, surprised at my frantic entrance, then quickly reached for my hand once she heard the nurse explaining that I should go do some bloodwork to indicate the probability of potential ovarian cancer. We both sat there, stunned. The doctor hadn't mentioned anything about the possibility of cancer. That had never crossed my mind prior to the call, but soon my mind was hijacked by that only thought.

I rushed to take the blood tests they asked for, leaving work as soon as we hung up the phone. I kept telling myself to breathe and that they were just being cautious. "The doctor said my symptoms suggest I have endometriosis. Surely, this mass is an endometrioma, so the tests won't indicate cancer. There's no need to worry."

Five days later, the results were in. The nurse called to say that both blood test results were elevated. Because of that, they canceled my upcoming excision surgery and referred me to a gynecologic oncology surgeon.

I was not expecting that. It all happened so fast and out of the blue, and my anxiety and fear were reaching their highest levels. My appointment with the gynecologic oncologist was two days later. He was caring and intelligent, and I felt like I was in capable hands. He said it was probably endometriosis, but that it could also be cancer. There was no way to know until he removed the mass and did a biopsy during surgery, which he scheduled for two weeks later. He explained the procedure: he would remove my left ovary with the mass in order to take it out intact. They would biopsy the tissue while I was on the operating room table, and if it was cancer, he would change from keyhole to open surgery. He would do a full hysterectomy and oophorectomy, in addition to removing any other cancer found. I would then need to start immediate chemotherapy.

The two weeks leading up to the surgery were a whirlwind of shock, disbelief, and fear. The gravity of the situation weighed heavy on me, and it was hard to think about anything else except the very real possibility that the large mass could be cancer. On the day of the surgery, I could hardly breathe, but I kept reminding myself to be present and in the moment. When I was in the Uber en route to the hospital, I counted the cars we drove past on the highway. When I was signing the consent forms, I focused on the weight of the pen against my hand. "Be in this moment," I told myself over and over.

As soon as I woke up from surgery, the nurse immediately said, "It wasn't cancer!" Although I was confused and groggy from the anesthesia, I understood and breathed a sigh of relief.

Once I was more alert, the nurse wheeled me to another room, where my mom and best friend were waiting. My mom showed me the pictures the surgeon gave her from the surgery and recounted what he had told her. "The mass was a large endometrioma," she said. "You have stage IV endometriosis. It's on your intestines too, and the doctor said you should reschedule your excision surgery for a few months from now, after your body recovers from this surgery."

For the next few hours, as my mom placed ice chips in my parched mouth, I asked her several times to repeat what the doctor had told her. I felt so incredibly relieved to know it wasn't cancer and validated to have a 100% confirmed diagnosis of the illness that took my life over at seventeen years old.

Self-Reflection

Write out a sentence or a few short sentences that you think would be beneficial to you during a flare or a challenging moment. For example:

I am safe.
I am still breathing.
There is hope.
Better days will come.

Write the sentences somewhere accessible, like on a small paper to keep in your wallet or in the notes app of your phone.

Now, slowly read it aloud to yourself, really taking in the reassurance. Set a daily alarm at a time when you will be able to take a break from what you are doing for a minute. This might be during the time you eat breakfast or when you first wake up. When the alarm goes off, look at your sentences and say them out loud to yourself.

If you make a habit of saying it while times are good, it will become much easier to call upon it for comfort and motivation when times are difficult.

65

AN ANCHOR IN THE STORM

Yoga has become my anchor of stability in this frightening storm called endometriosis. Others might feel this same way about running, quietly reading a book every evening, or eating dinner daily with a loved one. I started doing yoga a few years ago because I was looking for a low impact way to stretch my muscles, which were often in pain. There are different types of yoga, and I soon realized that I prefer Hatha Yoga for its slower pace and longer holding of the poses, which help me stretch. On days when my pain is severe, I switch to a form of yoga called Yoga Nidra that involves using pillows and blankets and settling into comfortable poses for deep relaxation.

I didn't like yoga when I first started it, but I continued to do it daily because it relaxed the tension in my body, reduced my dreadful hip and leg pain, and helped me sleep better. To my surprise, I fell in love with yoga over several months as I saw emotional benefits—it relaxed my mind as well as provided me a devoted time in my day for self-reflection. At some point, rolling out the yoga mat became something I could count on daily when other parts of my life felt completely out of control. Each day brings the unpredictable—

pain, nausea, fatigue, doctor's appointments, work stress, visits to the emergency room. Each day there is a rise of emotions in me, ranging from frustration to sadness to hopelessness. Doing yoga every morning is one of the only constants in my life.

At seven p.m. daily, shades drawn and in the dark, I'm alone with my feelings and just the flickering of a candle. Yoga is my chance to connect consciously to my body and to the stillness inside of me; it's an opportunity to bring my mind back to the present moment, to let go of my fears and bitterness, and to remember to breathe deeply. Even if I start the practice crying or infuriated because of a life circumstance that is upsetting me, the combination of movement and conscious breathing tends to help me ground myself, calm the swirl of thoughts in my head, and access a place of serenity inside me. Yoga has become part of my emotional self-care routine. It helps me nurture my heart and cope with situations that so often feel completely unacceptable to me.

The week leading up to my surgery for the mass, I was on my mat doing yoga every second that I wasn't at work. Yoga was the only thing that was helping me keep it together. As the surgery day approached and I prepared in advance for post-surgery recovery by buying supplies, preparing and freezing meals to eat in the difficult weeks afterwards, and moving everything down from the top shelves so I won't have to stretch, I was sinking further into terror of what could be in store for me.

I could suddenly feel, deep in my gut, how fragile life is. How quickly and easily things can change. The uncertainty. The impermanence. The dread. The fear.

I could barely breathe thinking about the possibility of the doctor saying, "You have cancer." If he did, my entire life as I knew it would change. All week long, thoughts of the worst-case scenario hijacked my mind: *What if it's cancer? What if it's not, but I have complications from the surgery that leave me worse than I am now?*

I was grateful that I had a yoga routine to turn to, one that I had strengthened over the past several years. It grounded me, anchoring me to the present moment. As my mind screamed with anxiety about the present situation, I brought myself back to my breath over and over again. *But what if...* My mind tortured me with many terrible possibilities about all that could go wrong during and after the surgery. On various occasions daily, I sat there on my yoga mat, letting the deep, murky waters of my feelings wash over me: Terror, overwhelming terror. Panic. I would sit quietly with the headache, the overwhelming urge to vomit, the rock in my stomach, the jittery sensations in my legs which wanted to get up and run and run but ironically also felt extremely heavy and paralyzed.

"Breathe," I would whisper to myself. I would put my hands down and feel the coolness of the yoga mat under me. "Breathe through the fear. Don't get wrapped up in the stories; don't go down those ugly paths. You have no idea what will happen, but whatever does, you will handle it, just like you always do."

Friends and coworkers were telling me that week that they were thinking of me, praying that it wasn't cancer. Outwardly, I thanked them for that, but inwardly, I wished they would instead pray that I find the strength to deal with whatever happens.

It no longer seems right to hope to be free from suffering when it is so universal around me. Yes, I want to be cancer-free; there's no denying that. But cancer is just one of many crises a person can face in a lifetime. It wasn't cancer, and that was a huge relief. But it might be cancer in several months or years from now, or some other enormous, life-changing challenge. Many people across the world are living their own darkest moments with grace, somehow finding it in themselves to genuinely smile in spite of their physical or emotional pain.

They hold their heads with dignity while waves of fear and the unknown suffocate their breath and constrict their chest. That is what I truly want: serenity, equanimity, courage.

So every day for those two weeks, I found myself on my yoga mat for hours in an attempt to calm my mind and find the courage to face my upcoming surgery.

Self-Reflection

- What helps you feel grounded or access a sense of serenity? Is there a place or activity that helps anchor you down or cope with the difficulties of endometriosis? If not, is there an activity you can think of that you can start?
- What is it about this that helps or will help you?
- What benefits does or will this provide you?

66

THE UNEXPECTED SILVER LININGS

Who would I be if I didn't have endometriosis?
I really don't know.

Endometriosis has been shaping me since I was a teenager, and if I hadn't gotten symptoms at such a young age, my life would probably look completely different than it does now. Endometriosis has influenced pretty much every aspect of my life, for better or for worse, since I was seventeen years old.

It's limited me in so many ways—the career I have, what I eat, what I do in my free time. Everywhere I look in my life, there are restrictions and deprivations. But having endometriosis has also shaped me in positive ways. My incapacitating period pain has made me more compassionate toward others and helped me find gratitude for the moments I'm not in pain. Being sick provides the opposite end of the spectrum; it gives me a comparison basis. Surprisingly, my life is richer for that.

Without endometriosis, I probably wouldn't have my sense of humor, which I cultivated to get through the dark and embarrassing moments. I don't think I would have truly committed to lifestyle habits that improved my overall health such as sleeping a minimum of eight hours a night or cutting out processed foods if excruciating pain wasn't lurking behind every action I take. I definitely wouldn't have done so much self-work because I wouldn't have *needed* to do it to try and cope with a disease that was ravaging my life.

Thank you, endometriosis, for forcing me to search inside of myself to find happiness when I couldn't find any in the outside world.

Thank you for shattering my perceptions of myself because it was only in feeling completely broken that I was able to find my true self.

Thank you for showing me that everything is impermanent and continually changing and that my time on this earth shouldn't be taken for granted.

Thank you, endometriosis, for all of your lessons. In trying to accept these sixteen years of hell, I've had to really search for hope to figure out how to live with frequent bouts of unbearable pain. To do so, I've had to go deep into my soul. I'm not sure if I would have embraced meditation, mindfulness, self-compassion, gratitude, forgiveness, or eliminating negative thought patterns if it weren't for endometriosis (or at least not with such dedication). Without so much suffering, I wouldn't have turned healing into a way of approaching my life.

It's strange to say that endometriosis has been my teacher. A thorn in my side, a knife in my bowels, the source of intense physical and emotional pain—but also a propeller to find meaning, joy, and self-understanding.

It has been a long, painful sixteen years, but it hasn't been spent in vain. It's a weird juxtaposition that such beautiful things have come out of something so horrifically ugly.

Dare I say that my illness, which has been such a heavy burden on my shoulders, has also had unexpected silver linings?

Self-Reflection

- Is there anything positive your illness and pain have brought you? For example, a community of people, character traits in yourself, or a commitment to personal lifestyle habits that improve your overall health?
- Has your illness motivated you to improve certain aspects of your life that you may not have otherwise?
- Looking at these positive life changes and/or anything else on your list, is it possible that your illness has also had any silver linings?
- If you find yourself saying "No" to all of these, that's okay. There is no pressure to feel that anything positive has come out of your illness. Do you think it's possible that one day your illness might bring you something positive? If so, what do you think you might need to potentially find a silver lining? For example, more time, more distance, or self-reflection on the possibility of it?

67

NO MATTER WHAT HAPPENS, I WILL BE OKAY

After another night of sleep was stolen from me by pain, I managed to finally doze off around five a.m. When I woke up, I saw that it was a beautiful, bright spring day; one that felt full of warmth, full of hope. I dressed and came outside, where I find myself now, lying on a blanket in the grass and looking up at the sky.

I've been so exhausted from my body being in post-surgery recovery and the demands of returning to work that I've had no time or energy to really process the whirlwind that these past few weeks have been. Now that I'm finally outside, I feel like I can breathe deeply for the first time since the nurse called me to say that I should see the gynecologic oncologist.

These last several weeks have made me acutely aware of my own mortality, but also aware of the life within me. It has awakened in me an important truth that has been trampled on and torn apart over years of suffering and fear: I am alive, and being alive is a gift! In this moment, I can feel this just intensely as I can feel the actual sun on my face.

It's hard to remember that life is a gift when I'm hunched over in pain, inside four walls with only my chairs and their lifeless gray striped pillows staring back at me. But outside, the grass is so green! How it dances in the breeze, growing imperceptibly under the rays of the sun. Life! It's everywhere. As soon as I get into an open field or a forest, I can feel it. It reminds me —I too am alive; I too am life!

I mustn't forget. I want to hold onto how precious life felt leading up to the surgery, but the joy of hearing it wasn't cancer is already beginning to fade under the stresses of everyday work, exhaustion, and pain. I close my eyes and place my hands gently on the grass, pressing down to feel the soft, cool touch of the soil beneath its blades. I can feel its life force like the beating of my heart. From here, life is born. The Earth is alive.

I am alive.

I vow to intentionally bring in daily gratitude for this fact. How precarious life is; how easily it can be lost.

I have no doubt that more pain-filled days and nights are on the horizon for me, but I also have no doubt that no matter what happens, I *will* be okay. A slight smile comes to my lips. I can see that the seeds of self-confidence and self-trust that I planted in my heart have taken root and the flowers that are blossoming are absolutely beautiful.

Self-Reflection

Can you get out into nature at any point in the next few weeks? Are you able to go for a walk in the woods, sit by the ocean, or pass a few minutes sitting in your yard, on a balcony looking toward the sky, or on a blanket in a park?

If you can't be outside, find a picture online of a beautiful nature scene, one that would relax you to be in. Or, recall a memory of a place outside that relaxes you. Take a moment to find that picture now or bring forward that memory before you continue reading. Visualize yourself there, be it standing in the waves, walking along the field, sitting on a fallen log. Really try to imagine yourself in the landscape you are looking at or recalling, and feel what it's like to be there.

- What's the temperature there? Is it warm, chilly, comfortable?
- Is there a breeze?
- What sounds are there?
- What sensations are there? How do the waves, grass, rocks, sand, or surface beneath your feet feel?
- Can you feel the strength, power, or aliveness of the earth?
- How you feel in your body—does being there help you feel lighter, more expansive, open, relaxed, alive, happy?

Take a few minutes to mindfully be with the earth, noticing the imagined landscape around you with all of your senses.

68

THE SURPRISING TRANSFORMATION

A creative writing piece on finding peace.

I find myself lying alone and naked, transplanted to a destitute landscape with no trees or shelter. I'm surrounded by dirt and thorny shrubs; the sky above is ominously black. I look down to see the familiar sword protruding from my abdomen.

I quickly recognize the barren scenery that stretches on endlessly. I have been here hundreds of times before—in the landscape of endometriosis pain. I watch as daggers begin to fall violently from the sky, but this time, just before they hit the ground, they surprise me—by turning into butterflies. The butterflies are gorgeous with vivid blues and greens, and they float away effortlessly back into the sky.

As these daggers continue to rain down and morph into butterflies, the clouds part and the sun shines, its warm rays washing over me. In the silence, I can hear the faint fluttering of a thousand butterfly wings. I reach my hand out to see if one will land on my palm. My patience pays off, and a few minutes later a butterfly alights, its legs tickling my skin. "You're beautiful," I say.

"So are you," it whispers before it flies back into the swirling kaleidoscope.

I imagine myself flying along with them, the gentle, carefree breeze carrying me through the air, with space and possibility in all directions. My attention comes back to the sword pinning me to the ground. I need to pull it out, I decide, so I take a deep breath, preparing myself. Suddenly, the sword begins to transform as magically and surprisingly as the butterfly daggers. The blade becomes leaf-wrapped stems rising out of the open wound of my abdomen, the hilt bursting into deep purple flowers. Their sweet aroma envelopes me, reminding me of the summers of my youth and a patch of wild violets near our family's house.

Tears come to my eyes at this turn of events. The daggers are butterflies, the sword a bunch of flowers? What is happening? What does all of this mean? The landscape of endometriosis has somehow morphed from a barren, desperate, hopeless land to one that has surprising and unexpected beauty among the long stretches of emptiness.

Is the change because I've been learning how to stop getting caught up in my fear? Is my mind showing me that I no longer need to be terrified of the pain? Is this an example of the beautiful relief that self-forgiveness can provide my tormented soul? Is it happening to show me that some moments of suffering can transform into beauty through the growth and wisdom it brings us? Is it because I've been learning that we put our own personal meaning on everything that happens to us?

As I lie here contemplating this, I realize that as interesting as it would be to understand why this landscape is different today, it's really not important right now. Bringing awareness back to the present moment, I turn my face toward the breeze and breathe in the sweetness of the violets. The butterflies swirl in the sky as the sun warms my face.

I am here. I am alive. I am present. I don't understand it all, but I embrace it with open arms. Even if there were still a sword pinning me down at this moment, it wouldn't seem to matter.

I am already free.

Self-Reflection

- What does freedom mean to you?
- Do you feel free? If so, why? If not, is there some part of your life that you want freedom from—a job, your illness, a relationship, a feeling, or a thought?
- What is it about this thing that makes you feel in need of freedom?
- Do you feel trapped, suffocated, or weighed down?
- What is something you can do to help you take a step closer to feeling free?
- Can you take that step today, or write down a time that you will act on that step?

69

FINDING COMPASSION TOWARD MYSELF

The night before the surgery for the mass, I found myself choking on my sobs as I got into bed, unable to stop crying, lying there both in literal and emotional darkness.

Thoughts ran through my mind: "I deserve to have cancer for all of the terrible things that I've done. I'm being punished; it's my fault for not being a better person."

I found myself deep down the rabbit hole of my past. I cringed and cried as I thought of the person I became after getting sick. Before my symptoms started, I had an excellent sense of humor, but after a few months of chronic pain, I no longer knew how to laugh. My lips forgot how to smile as all the joy disappeared from my life one cramp at a time. After having to quit all of my hobbies, complaining became the one thing I was good at. In my mind, everything was going wrong. How I made known to everyone the misery my life circumstances were causing me! The injustice of dealing with pain, nausea, and fatigue 24/7 filled me with rage. At the same time, I felt like everything happening was somehow my fault, and self-blame started rotting me at my core.

The carefree Amy whose eyes lit up with happiness when

around friends was gone, replaced by an angry victim who complained about every little thing. I got stuck in my irritation and frustration with the world, stuck in my sadness. I also became very focused on myself as I struggled to survive the onslaught of symptoms; I was unable to give caring attention or a listening ear to those around me.

Within a few months, I started losing the friends that I hadn't realized I'd pushed away. At that time, it hurt deeply, each abandonment twisting the knife of loneliness deeper into my heart. Looking back, I understand that I was not coping well with being sick and my new bitter attitude was surely hard to be around.

On that night before the surgery, as I remembered the various ways I 'failed' at being a good friend, and 'failed' at coping and life in general, shame overcame me. In some moments, I found myself completely identifying with the guilt washing over me. "I deserve to be sick," I would think. In other moments, I was able to take a step back, saying out loud, "Self-blame. Self-criticism," and bringing in self-compassion to gently hold my hand. That battle with myself played out until I finally fell asleep, completely exhausted.

Looking back today at that dark night, without the fear of cancer on my shoulders, I can recall my past and gently say to myself, "It's okay that you acted like that. It really is." It was an overwhelming, terrifying, confusing time for a young person of seventeen years old. I am so harsh with myself for not having handled my onset of symptoms with dignity nor grace. How easily I spiral into thoughts of self-criticism and beating myself up for the 'awful' person that I was.

It's true that for many years, I didn't handle getting sick well. But what defines handling it 'well' or 'poorly' when dealing with an all-consuming chronic illness? Contrary to what I subconsciously believe, there is no right or wrong way to get through a crisis—or my life, for that matter. Yes, there were days when I complained nonstop and others when I was too overwhelmed to get up from crying for hours on the floor. There were days when I felt so emotionally drained that I couldn't even bring myself to get out of bed and brush my teeth. But that's what I needed on those days to cope and to survive the soul-wrenching moments. Can I let go of judging my past? It's true that my life and my reactions to it have been messy, imperfect, and complex —but that's natural and a part of being human.

What's not very common is to handle a huge obstacle right off the bat with dignity and grace—so why do I expect this of myself? I haven't given myself much room to make mistakes. And why do I keep looking at my past and calling the way I acted a mistake? My mind loves to berate myself for not having had all the answers, for having made poor choices, for having acted a certain way or not acted a certain way. I continuously demand perfection of myself, and when I obviously haven't been perfect (because no one is!), I've taken it as evidence of the terrible person that I am. But that is ridiculous. I *am* a good person. I may not feel like one, but I am one. I may not have always acted in the way I would act now, but that's because I didn't know everything that I know now. I did the best that I could; I dealt with those situations the *only* way I knew how at the time. I can't change the past, but I am actively changing the way I handle things now.

I thought that over this past year I had come to let go of these false beliefs that my illness is a punishment for being a 'bad' person, but this incident has shown me that the emotional wound is still there. However, it's not as deep as it used to be. That night before my surgery, as my mind ran wild with thoughts about how I deserved to be sick, I was able to somewhat counter them by imagining my kind, loving grandma with me. In my mind's eye, she hugged me tightly, just as she had done when I was a child and upset about something. "It's okay, honey," she said.

"No, it's not," I sobbed in her imaginary arms. "I probably have cancer because I'm so awful."

"No," she said gently. "You're not awful. Let go of this idea. Forgive yourself. Carrying around that hatred toward yourself is so heavy. You're a good person—you just aren't used to saying that about yourself, but it's true. You don't need to be ashamed of yourself or who you were. You were learning and growing—that's what living is about. Each mistake moves you forward; each experience helps shape you into the person you want to be. It's okay that you acted the ways that you did. You're a good person, you hear me? Keep saying it to yourself, and one day you'll know this truth in your heart."

Self-Reflection

- Have you done anything that you consider negative or that you regret?
- How does it make you feel to think about this?
- Do you view it as evidence of your inadequacy or of the 'bad person' that you are?
- Looking back from an objective view, what caused you to do those things? Were you simply overwhelmed? Would others have acted the same way if they were thrown into that situation?
- How do you, or could you, bring in compassion for yourself?
- Think of someone or something full of love. This could be a friend; a family member; a pet; a religious figure, like Jesus or the Buddha; a world leader, like Gandhi or the Dalai Lama. See yourself through their eyes, and the forgiveness and compassion they offer you. What might they say to you? Would they hug you or hold your hand?

70

A CRUEL TWIST OF FATE

Exactly four months after the surgery to remove the endometrioma and my ovary, I had excision surgery,[1] the gold standard for endometriosis care. Recovering from the two surgeries has been a long, slow process, but I'm taking it day by day and being gentle with myself.

It's now been five months since I had excision. I never believed that this would be true for me, but many of my endometriosis symptoms have drastically improved. I can see there's still a long road ahead though. My body needs to heal after more than a decade of high inflammation and pain, and additionally, there is still a lot I need to treat. I can see more than ever that endometriosis is a disease that affects the full body, and its common co-conditions continue to be present.

I'm still having urinary frequency, urgency, and burning, so I need to address my Interstitial Cystitis. I hope to do pelvic floor therapy at some point, to help with these bladder symptoms as well as my referred leg pain.

I tested positive for small intestinal bacterial overgrowth (SIBO), and my stool sample also came back with high levels of opportunistic bacteria and gut dysbiosis in the large intestine.

Both of those need treating and hopefully after my gut bacteria is healthy again, my large, bloated 'endobelly' will go down.

While I'm having much less pain with eating and no pain any longer with bowel movements, I'm still experiencing shooting pains in my rectum if I eat starchy or fibrous foods. This might be because the excision surgeon intentionally left behind around 5% of my endometriosis in my rectum (rather than do a bowel resection as he felt the risks in my specific case at that time outweighed the benefit).

After losing my left ovary, my hormones have dropped to menopausal levels, and I'm having hot flashes, insomnia, and brain fog; my period is now coming every twenty-one days.

There is still a lot to address and recover from, but I'm thrilled that my endometriosis pain, inflammation, and fatigue has reduced considerably. The biggest improvement, and definitely most shocking, is that I haven't had a single bout of debilitating pain. Although my first period after my excision surgery was rough, when I got my second period, I broke down sobbing with joy and amazement at how little pain I felt. My periods still have me dizzy, bleeding heavily, and fatigued, but the difference in the pain is incredible. I find it truly unbelievable that I'm not bedridden for days; I'm not vomiting, hyperventilating, or passing out on the bathroom floor from pain. Sometimes, as I do yoga and press my forehead to the floor in child's pose, I break down sobbing with gratitude. "Thank you," I whisper, "for alleviating me of that excruciating pain." Getting into bed at night, I place my hands over my heart for a few seconds and breathe in deeply. "Thank you."

As I've been recovering from the surgery, life was starting to feel different—lighter and more carefree than it had in sixteen years. But just as I was finally allowing myself to believe that my quality of life was actually improving, the universe decided to play a twisted joke on me. I know logically that isn't true—the Fates are not up in the sky laughing at me. But with what has happened, I'm once more fighting thoughts of "Why me?" as if the universe has some kind of personal vendetta against me.

I've recently been diagnosed with histamine intolerance, and the doctor is doing tests to see if it's from a condition called mast cell activation syndrome.[2] Histamine intolerance can cause severe reactions ranging from migraines, tachycardia (racing heart), dizziness, insomnia, itchy hives, and even anaphylaxis. I'm now having *all* of these reactions, and they are being caused by pretty much *everything*. It began with food but within several weeks, it progressed to painkillers, soap, makeup, nail polish, shampoo, heat, cold, stress, movement, sunlight, strong emotions, perfumes, candles, exercise, and sex—to name a few. I'm completely overwhelmed and my heart feels like it has been torn in half by my grief that my life is returning to its pre-surgery state of triggers and debilitating flares. Once more, I have as many limitations as before, except with routine activities like eating leftovers, washing my hair, and being in the sun added to the list of 'things that give me (now a completely different kind of) flares.'

Histamine symptoms are much different than endometriosis, but ironically, they are turning out to be just as devastating. It's beautiful that sex doesn't hurt anymore, but having it causes me hours of tachycardia. The endometriosis fatigue has been replaced by insomnia—so I'm exhausted all day anyway since I'm unable to sleep at night. Sadly, even eating is still difficult! My bowel is no longer fused to my pelvic sidewall from endometriosis adhesions, so I can eat a wider variety of foods than when my bowel was narrowed. But if my histamine 'bucket' fills up from whatever I'm eating (and there's no way to predict when it will fill), then food randomly causes anaphylaxis so I have to carry around an epinephrine autoinjector.

I feel deep gratitude to have had excision surgery. Due to various reasons, such as the small number of surgeons who are trained to do such complex surgery, insurance hurdles, and lack of access, excision surgery is an absolute privilege that the majority of endometriosis patients worldwide aren't able to receive. I am conscious of how extremely lucky I was to find a surgeon in my city under my insurance plan. I am incredibly thankful that I received the gold standard treatment for endometriosis and that my surgeon was able to remove 95% of my endometriosis. I am amazed and overjoyed that the severe endometriosis pain that has haunted me since I was a teenager is finally gone. Is this only temporary? Will that pain return? I don't know, but at this moment, I am trying not to get caught up in my worries of the future and instead focus on where I am right now—without severe pain for the first time in sixteen years.

But at times, my deep gratitude is overshadowed by anger and grief. I'm shocked and overwhelmed by these unexpected new health problems. The weight of this situation is heavy on my shoulders, and I'm finding it hard to breathe (and not just because of the episodes of anaphylaxis). I'm barely coping right now, and I feel completely lost. All I can do is put one foot in front of the other and wait for this metaphorical winter to turn into spring.

Self Reflection

- What kind of metaphorical season are you in right now? For example, are you in a dark winter, a hopeful spring, or a happy summer?
- How long have you been in it?
- How does it feel to be in this season?
- Are you wishing it will end soon or hoping it will last?

71

A MESSAGE TO MYSELF

It shocks me to think about how young so many of us are when we first get sick. No one is ever ready to begin to step into doctor's offices, to suffer agonizing pain, to face the confusion, fear, and exhaustion of trying to get a diagnosis and treatment for a chronic disease. To be ripped out of adolescence and into the dark world of endometriosis was terrifying.

I remember being seventeen years old, in high school and suddenly having to do blood tests, colonoscopies, and MRI scans. While I was in the waiting room of the fourth doctor's office that I went to, I thought to myself, "Please let them cure me; I don't want my problems to be chronic."

It turns out that my problems are indeed chronic, but things have improved over the years as I've learned to live with them. I wish my thirty-three-year-old self could go back to that terrified seventeen-year-old girl and hug her tightly. I would tell her that, eventually, she would be okay. I would tell her that there would be horrible, hopeless, desperate times ahead, but also beautiful ones filled with love, curiosity, and meaning. I would tell her that no matter how unendurable the pain, she would always make it to the other side. I would tell her how proud I am of her for always doing her best, even during the confusing, overwhelming moments. I would tell her how brave she is because even in the darkest, most unbearable moments, she somehow pulled through.

And she will keep pulling through.

Self-Reflection

- Think back to a moment when you were scared and uncertain of what the future held. Write a letter directly to your younger self, using second person language. (Example: **you** can, **you** did, **you** are.) What would you say to your younger self?
- Do you feel proud of her/him/them?
- Can you reassure or comfort her/him/them?
- Can you highlight the qualities she has/he has/they have that have gotten her/him/them through the dark times?
- Can you see how much she has/he has/they have changed or grown since then?
- When you are finished, read this letter out loud to yourself. How does it make you feel to speak to your past self?

72

BEAUTY IN THE FACE OF FEAR

I find myself thinking a lot about the days leading up to the surgery for the endometrioma. That was already several months ago, but I still vividly remember them as if they were yesterday. It was a terrifying and overwhelming week, but surprisingly, it was also extraordinarily beautiful. I felt profound appreciation that I had those sweet, simple days to enjoy before everything potentially turned upside down. My job, my routine, the grocery shopping and chores—it usually feels mundane, but that week it felt special. Every ordinary thing seemed precious because the threat of a twelve centimeter cancerous mass on my ovary had me acutely aware of how brief, fleeting, and impermanent life is.

I didn't rush through that week. As my coworkers were wishing out loud that it was the weekend and that Monday would turn into Friday, I was wishing the opposite. With surgery in just a few days, I wanted time to slow down so that I wouldn't miss a single second of my life. If I were to have advanced stage ovarian cancer, then my time would possibly be running out. Even though I was still in pain and fatigued, I was cherishing every moment before the surgery, paying attention, awake and alive—perhaps more than I've ever been during my entire life.

A few days before the surgery, I fried an egg for breakfast and instead of impatiently wanting it to cook quickly so I could eat it, I just watched calmly as it changed from a liquid to a solid in the pan. The bright yolk sat on the white of the egg, a perfect yellow circle. Watching that egg fry was an impromptu lesson in impermanence. In just a few minutes, that egg was different than before. And yet, it was still perfect.

I ate that egg slowly, enjoying its taste and texture. Washing the dishes afterward, the water felt warm against my fingers. The soap suds sparkled in the sink; bubbles arose and dissolved among the foam. After, I went into the living room, admiring the shadow the chair cast on the wall from the weak morning sunlight. I still remember how I sat down and looked around, admiring the intricate details of the ordinary that surrounded me.

It wasn't all beautiful, of course. At least twice a day I would break down sobbing, my chest heavy with fear. I would go to the yoga mat and bring myself through various sun salutations (a sequence of yoga poses), reminding myself to breathe and noting what I felt out loud: "Fear. Fear. Fear."

It was strange to oscillate from being terrified of the future to being incredibly overjoyed to be alive right then, but I stayed with the feelings. I would sit with the fear until it lessened, until I no longer feel overwhelmed and like the world was collapsing in on me. Then, I was able to be with the present moment: the books on my shelves (and the dust), the wrinkles in the blanket on the bed, the potato on the counter that had begun to sprout. I would see it all with so much love in my heart for this life that it would start to overwhelm me, and the fear of losing it all would creep back in. Back to the mat I would go to ground myself.

That week was a roller coaster of emotions. I also laughed so hard—to the point of my abdomen hurting—at how ridiculous

I've been to care about the silliest, most trivial problems: how upset I've gotten in the past over itchy bug bites, my hair getting frizzy in the rain, or the copy machine at work always being out of paper whenever I needed to print. None of it matters! How I've wasted so much of my energy, my lifeforce, on the unimportant! But instead of berating myself, I just kindly said out loud, "It's okay. You didn't know."

On and off the yoga mat I went all day long, at times breathing shallowly in fear; at others, deeply and slowly in gratitude. I vowed that no matter what the future held, I would never forget that week: that horrible, fantastic, heavy, lighthearted, distressing, joyous week that was passing by at a snail's pace and also at the speed of light. That week reinforced in me what I had been learning over the past few years—that life's beauty is accessible to me when I live in the present, even in the most upsetting of times.

Sixteen years ago, my illness swept me off the ground with the force of a tsunami, and I was barely afloat while the sea threw me about. But at some point, I began learning how to cultivate a serenity that can anchor me down; I began learning how to swim among the waves of life instead of drowning. I'm *still* learning how to live among these choppy waves, but as I change, the water is also changing. I never would have guessed that the same ocean of life which so often terrifies me could also be breathtakingly beautiful.

Self-Reflection

Imagine that you meet a genie that can give you one of two wishes: feeling better (including no longer having endometriosis or any chronic illnesses) *or* always being able to find happiness and beauty in your life. This genie can grant you either wish right now.

- What would you choose? Why?
- How important do you think mindset is for living with chronic illness?
- Do you think it's possible to be facing a difficult time and still find gratitude?

73

GOODBYE, DOLLY

The year I lived in the rainforest, I had very little in my cabin but everything with me was vital: my umbrella and rain boots for the rain; one sweater for the the rare occasions when the temperature dropped; eight pairs of underwear, one to last each day until I could hand wash them on Saturday; two pairs of pants and five shirts. For toiletries, I had a shampoo bar that doubled as body soap, deodorant, eyedrops, floss, toothpaste, and a toothbrush. I had a flashlight, a candle, a lighter, a mosquito net, a notepad, a pen, and a few books. It had all fit in a backpack, and it was enough. With these few items, my needs were met.

While I don't plan on getting rid of everything I currently own to such a level of minimalism, I do want a simpler life. I want less to clean, less to take care of, less on my shelves. Life with chronic illness is complicated, and I often feel weighed down. The pain, the fatigue, the emotional burden—it's all so heavy. I don't want to also be crushed by tons of belongings in my apartment that I never use or items that bring up painful memories for me. I want to open up space to breathe easier and feel less stressed without what feels like clutter to me.

I've been going through all my things, focusing on one room each weekend, evaluating what I actually use and what brings me joy. It's been surprisingly relaxing to look through my stuff, examining each item, thinking critically about whether I want to keep it or if I only have it out of nostalgia or habit.

I've already made four boxes for donations, with my tennis racket in one of them. I haven't used it in years and if I'm honest with myself, I probably won't ever use it again. It doesn't hurt to say that anymore; I have new hobbies that bring meaning to my life.

Today, I'm looking at everything in the bedroom. My dolly is on the bed in her usual spot. Her pink hair is somewhat matted after a decade of comforting me daily, her green nurse's outfit wrinkled and faded. I pick her up and trace the words on her dress with my finger. *Get well soon.* How much hope those words gave me at times and how much they taunted me at others.

But what about now? Do I still need my dolly? A twinge of guilt comes over me just thinking that, as well as apprehension to donate a doll that I have felt superstitious about for so many years. Not to mention that I feel a lot of uncertainty, and even despair, with my new histamine problems. Will I ever 'get well soon'? Probably not. While I hold onto hope that I will continue to improve my health, realistically, I don't think I will ever feel as well as a healthy person without chronic illness does.

Some part of me feels that perhaps it's time to let go of my dolly and say goodbye. She has been a symbol of my hopes and dreams: for many years, all I wanted *was* to 'get well soon'. But now? I think I want something different. I care more about finding meaning, cultivating gratitude, and experiencing joy. I still want to get well, of course, but I think I've finally come to terms with the fact that my illness is chronic and incurable.

"My dolly," I say, my tears welling up as I look into her blue eyes, "Thank you for always being there for me, for never leaving me, for never judging me. At times, you were my only comfort during moments of pain. You lived my pain with me; you hugged me while I cried. Thank you for your constant, unwavering support."

I hug her to my chest. "You've helped me through the darkest moments of my life. I've loved you so much, but it's time for us both to move on. But don't you worry about me—I've learned how to be there for myself."

Very carefully, I set my dolly on the top of one of the boxes destined for donations. She looks at me from the box, quietly, calmly, stoically, like she always does. I think she understands what's happening. *Get well soon,* her outfit reads.

"I am," I told her. "I am getting well on all levels of health, although it's slow-going at times and there are unexpected setbacks. And I promise you that I will continue to do so."

I trace the letters on her dress one last time before closing the lid of the box.

Self-Reflection

- Do the items in your home have an emotional impact on you?
- How do you feel when you look at areas that you consider are cluttered?
- How do you feel when you look at areas of open space?
- Do you tend to hold onto many sentimental items?
- Do you find it easy or hard to get rid of things you own?
- Do you have items that you no longer use or that no longer bring you joy? This could be clothing, shoes, purses, kitchen appliances, decorations, books,

ornaments, furniture, photo albums, DVDs, children's toys, or anything else.

- If you have any such items, what would you like to do with them? Do you think you'd feel freer or lighter if they were no longer in your home, such as if you donated them to a good cause?
- If you do decide to donate/recycle/trash any of the items you found, if anything has a personal meaning attached to it, give yourself the time you might need to come to terms with parting with it.

74

THE CHANGING OF THE SEASONS

The histamine intolerance situation has pushed me deep down all the familiar rabbit holes: rage, indignation, injustice, sadness, fear, desperation. My mind is turning to all the usual stories:

Of course this happened to me.
What did I do to deserve this?
I'm never going to feel better.
This is somehow my fault.

But this time, I've been recognizing them as exactly that—untrue stories invented by my mind. They are definitely seductive, and sometimes I am pulled into feeling extremely sorry for myself, or worse, hating myself. After a while, I manage to catch myself in those thought patterns and say out loud, "Victim mentality" or "Self-blame. Self-judgment."

At the onset of my histamine symptoms, I sank into a profound sadness, but my expression of despair was different than it initially was with endometriosis. I didn't try to avoid it through unhealthy coping mechanisms like I had turned to throughout my teens and twenties. I was (and still am) acknowledging and accepting the emotions that have come forward, inviting them in for tea. I'm allowing myself to feel them fully: I've screamed in rage into pillows; I've cried uncontrollably for hours over the course of several weeks, mourning the loss of the idea that post-surgery my life would get easier. I've reached out to a mental health professional so I can speak to someone about how devastated I feel. I'm also journaling, meditating, and sitting in self-compassion with my feelings. The lessons I've been learning in trying to find peace with endometriosis are helping guide me through this new health crisis.

Even so, for the first few months after the histamine symptoms began, I was hanging on emotionally by a thread. Every aspect of my life changed; my world seemed like it was falling apart. I didn't feel capable of talking above a whisper when coworkers interacted with me; I was ducking under my desk in my cubicle several times a day so the tears could roll down my cheeks unnoticed when someone walked by. As soon as I would get home from work, I would wrap my arms around myself in a tight hug and soothe that scared part of me. I would draw the shades, sit on my bed, and rock back and forth, telling myself out loud, "You will be okay."

Incredibly, about five months after the onset of these horrible symptoms, I am starting to be okay. Physically no—the symptoms haven't diminished at all. Emotionally though, I'm coping much better. I'm starting to find the place inside of me where I can say: This is hard. It breaks my heart. I don't like it—but it is what it is. No matter how much I don't want this to be my life, it *is* my life right now. This *is* what is before me, and denial and wishful thinking won't change my reality. So I'm making every attempt to live in peace *with* my new condition. Part of that process is looking for ways to manage the symptoms instead of simply hating my life. For example:

Wide awake from insomnia? The calm, quiet darkness of the

night is a great time to meditate. I bring up a guided meditation on my phone, close my eyes, and let myself relax to the sound of the teacher's soothing voice.

Exhausted at work? I head to my car and recline the seats, reaching for my earplugs, eye mask, pillow, and blanket. With the relentless insomnia, these daily midmorning naps are keeping me functioning.

Hives? Vipassana meditation taught me well. Don't itch; don't scratch. The sensations will fade just as they arise.

I'm not going to lie—it's a lot. But these tactics are working much better for me than what I was doing these last few months: panicking at four a.m. that I wasn't asleep and would have to get up in just a few hours for work, trying to power through my workday while dizzy and nauseous from lack of sleep, and itching hives until they bled.

I'm deeply sad and my soul still hurts about these histamine problems, but I'm less overwhelmed. I've researched and adjusted my lifestyle and my diet to help as much as I can, but, like with endometriosis, lifestyle and diet can only do so much. I'm also working with a doctor who is knowledgeable in histamine intolerance and mast cell activation syndrome to address potential root causes, like hormones and gut health. He believes that with treatment my severe symptoms will become manageable, and this has given me some hope.

Every time I feel sorry for myself, I shrug my shoulders. The physical movement helps me somewhat to shake off the intrusive thoughts of "Why me?" that love to creep into my mind constantly, like during work meetings or in the produce section of the grocery store.

Don't get me wrong—this new 'oh well' attitude of mine is not apathy or denial. Rather, I'm trying to shift from anger and hatred of the situation toward neutrality. I don't want to get stuck in resentment and sadness for years, as I did with endometriosis. I've learned that burying emotions only allows them to fester, so I've let myself to be angry, sad, and hateful of this situation. I gave myself the time and space I needed to feel everything and anything that came up, without pressuring myself to feel a certain way or to 'get over it.' Now, after several months of fully feeling a broad range of emotions about these awful new circumstances, I'm ready to move forward.

I keep telling myself, "If I have a flare, then I have a flare." I don't want to get wrapped up in stories about these symptoms. I want to feel as neutral about them as I do about the color of the sky. I don't care about the color of the sky—it doesn't bother me, fluster me, or make me feel sad or angry or deprived. This same acceptance is what I want with this new condition that I now have to live with. I'm nowhere near there yet, but with each passing day, I'm getting a little closer. Even if it's only 0.1%, it's still a move in the right direction. And if I regress, if I spend a day in a flare and start to feel resentment and anger come in, that's okay—I allow myself to feel it, I acknowledge it, and I continue moving forward tomorrow.

"Hello," I'm saying to my insomnia, to my dizziness, to the feeling of my throat closing, to my hives, to my migraines, to my racing heart, to my flares. "Welcome to my life. I hope you don't stay too long, but while you are here, let's coexist in peace."

Self-Reflection

- How would you define coexisting in peace with your symptoms? What would that look like in your life?
- Are you currently coexisting in peace with any of them?
- Have you ever coexisted in peace with any symptoms?
- Are there any steps you could start to take to help you coexist in peace with your symptoms?

75

I WILL BE OKAY WITHOUT ANYTHING CHANGING

Acceptance. It's a gift to my exhausted self. It's the sunlight that revives my shriveled, dying soul back to life, rescuing me from the lonely darkness. In this messy, imperfect process of finding peace, the volume is once more being turned down on how emotionally shattered I am by my circumstances. In acceptance, there is freedom, and it is beautiful.

This ongoing journey of acceptance has shown me that I will be okay, even if nothing ends up changing. I've learned tools to cope with the devastating moments, from mindfulness to gratitude to simply just remembering to take deep breaths. I've learned that even with chronic illness, I can live a meaningful, purposeful life, filled with love, belonging, and joy. While I'm not okay now, I trust that in time, as I continue to learn to be with these new symptoms and shift toward neutrality, I *can and will* be okay.

I know now that I will be okay when I'm flaring.
That I will be okay when I'm in pain.
That I will be okay when I am too fatigued to get out of bed.
That I will be okay when I'm nauseous.

That I will be okay when the day isn't going as I'd hoped.
That I will be okay when it's the fifth month in a row I feel absolutely miserable.
That I will be okay when I have to cancel my plans again.
That one day, as I continue to find peace, I can and will be okay with things *exactly how they are.*

Illness might still have my physical body, but it no longer has a hold on my mind and my soul. I know now that I have only a fleeting moment to be alive. Who knows when this life could be taken from me? Life is painful, draining, burdensome, and catastrophic at times, but it's also exhilarating, glorious, awe-inspiring, and beautiful. The human experience is all of these. It's a spectrum from suffering to joy, and there is no cherry-picking my experience. There are seasons in life: times when things are bright and cheery, like the springtime with its flowers blooming and temperatures rising, and there are times of harsh, relentless winters when everything is frozen, bleak, and depressing.

My life cannot always be springtime. That would be unnatural; that would go against the laws of the universe. Light cannot exist without darkness, springtime without winter, happiness without sadness. Life is 10,000 joys *and* 10,000 sorrows. I'm ready to embrace it all with open arms because I finally trust that no matter how difficult life gets, if I face it with an open heart then I will have the strength to get through anything.

When we look at all we have been through, when we see our scars, think of our worst flares, or our darkest moments, we can also think about how *we got through all of them.* We are *getting* through all of them, one day at a time, or even simply—like in moments of desperate, backbreaking pain—one second at a time.

That is what we do. We handle tough situations. We get

through the unbearable. We put one foot in front of the other, moment after moment, crisis after crisis, flare after flare, and we keep going. We do the things that scare us, whether it's facing our periods or getting out of bed in the morning.

We *will* get through all of these challenges that our health brings. And as we do, we will learn a lot about life and even more about ourselves. As endometriosis cracks open our souls, we can explore the deepest layers of life, healing, and ourselves that we may have never discovered otherwise.

Self-Reflection

Do you think you can be okay with your symptoms? Make a list of all of the symptoms that bother you. Now, go down the list and say about each symptom, "I can be okay when I __________." For example, "I can be okay when I have fatigue / have nausea / am in pain." Pay attention to what you feel as you say these sentences.

- How do you feel when you say them? For example, do you feel embarrassed, confident, ridiculous, angry, unsure?
- Do you get any sensations in your stomach, like a knot or butterflies?
- How is your breathing when you say them—it is normal, or are you breathing slower or faster?
- Do you say them loudly or in a quiet tone?
- How does this activity feel to you? Is it hard to do this activity? Does it feel like it could one day be the truth?

See if you can do this activity every day for a week and pay attention to any changes in how you feel. For example, do you start to soften toward the activity? Does it get easier? Does it help you start to believe that this could be true for you?

76

WEATHERING THE STORM

When I first got sick and was jolted from my comfortable, everyday routine, I felt powerless as my life turned into a confusing, overwhelming mess; I was clueless about how to help myself. Thrown into the endometriosis tornado, I struggled desperately while the storm violently tossed me around.

When it threw me back on the ground, I was completely lost. I barely had the strength to move; I had no idea where I was or which direction to go in. Slowly, I found ways to drag myself to my feet and take as many steps as I could toward the clear sky in the distance. Before long, the storm would slam me down again, but each time, I would get up and once again move forward as much as I could.

Without even realizing it, these awful, unwanted experiences helped me grow stronger, and one day I realized that the wind was no longer knocking me down. Not because the wind was less powerful than before but because *I* was now better able to withstand its fury. Sometimes, there are moments when the storm lets up, and I find myself in the calm, gentle sunlight. I look around at the destruction, shocked at all that I have made it through.

The young girl initially swept up into the whirlwind of disease is now unrecognizable to me. Then again, how could I expect to be the same carefree person I was sixteen years ago before I knew such a depth of suffering and pain?

With endometriosis, we have been through so much, but we are also some of the strongest, most resilient people I have ever had the privilege of knowing. I think about you all, my endo-family out there, having a hard time, suffering in pain, and I realize that I am not alone. I realize that I, too, have the strength you have, just like you have the same strength that I have.

I thank you for reading this book, for inspiring me, for helping me to keep going. In those moments when I want to give up, your collective strength pushes me to keep walking forward, one step at a time.

Although new storms are before me now, I somehow just *know* that I will make it to the other side, just as I have done during these years of debilitating endometriosis symptoms. I *will* find my way through this raging, destructive storm, even if it's crawling inch by inch. Because if there is one thing that endometriosis has taught me, it's that people with endometriosis can get through anything.

Self-Reflection

Define 'resilience' in your own words. What does this mean to you personally? There is no right or wrong, and your definition doesn't have to match that of the dictionary.

Has your resilience increased since you began dealing with endometriosis? If you don't think it has, can you think of at least one quality of yours that has (such as kindness, compassion, tenacity, patience, determination, problem solving skills) and define what that quality means to you personally?

EPILOGUE – WHAT NEXT?

There isn't one path for everyone, but we do have common building blocks. Practices like mindfulness, meditation, gratitude, yoga, qigong, journaling, speaking to a mental health professional, finding meaning, and changing our self-talk—these can all be a foundation for finding peace.

What do you feel *you* need in your life?

Maybe you are in a place where you are rushing all the time. If your mind is usually in the past or the future, practicing mindfulness could be good for you to work on being in the present moment. This may potentially help you find gratitude, have more joy, or notice and appreciate any moments you aren't in pain.

Maybe you realize that your self-talk is vicious and that you are harsh and judgmental with yourself. Practicing meditation could help you take a step back from your thoughts and observe them instead of getting so wrapped up and identified with them. Then, if you have a thought like "I'm a burden," you would no longer immediately believe it's true (which it's not!) This allows you to look at the idea and examine it, asking yourself, "Why do I think this? When did I start believing this? Is this the truth?" Meditation may help you separate yourself from the stories in your mind and construct a new and accurate narrative about yourself.

Maybe you are dealing with trauma, heavy emotions, or a lack of support. Seeing a qualified mental health professional, as well as journaling, may help you work through your emotions, feel supported and less alone, and organize chaotic thoughts so that you can express yourself fully.

These are just a few of many practices that can help you begin to find peace and think about yourself and your life differently. There is a wide variety of mindset exercises available online and for free. There are several different types of yoga and meditation styles; if a specific teacher or a certain therapist doesn't suit you, there are many more to choose from!

It can take a while to figure out what you like, but once you find something, stick to it for a few months. It's common to get frustrated and quit something when we don't see immediate improvement, but change takes time. Usually, the longer we practice something, the more benefits we see. Luckily, we don't have to spend all day doing any of these building blocks; just the habit of having these practices is powerful. Even fifteen minutes a day can be enough time to see changes in ourselves in just a few weeks or months. It may seem insignificant to name three things we are grateful for before going to bed each night, or to write about our feelings in a journal for ten minutes daily, but when we commit to practices like these, it can truly be transformative.

Sometimes, just starting can be the hardest part. Have you begun taking steps to find peace or neutrality? If so, what have you been doing? How has it been going?

When you are ready (there is no rush; it's your path and yours alone), what new practices do you want to add in?

If you are newly stepping onto this path, what is something that interests you where you might start? It could be any of the exercises from the self-reflections or anything you think of that you feel would help you get a step closer to peace. Can you start today to commit even just a few minutes to this activity daily? Where can you learn more information about it?

I invite you to try something once a week for fifteen minutes and go from there. I started with mindfulness, but you can pick anything that calls to you!

CONNECT WITH ME

If you want to reach out to me, please do! I'd love to hear from you. You can connect with me on Instagram or via the email on my website www.insixteenyears.com

On my website, I provide several resources for topics like gratitude, meditation, and self-compassion. Additionally, I have resources there for reputable websites and books on endometriosis, interstitial cystitis, histamine intolerance, and more!

You can also follow my podcast, ***In Sixteen Years of Endometriosis***, which I co-host with my best friend Brittany. We laugh, cry, and shout as we talk about all things endometriosis. We pride ourselves on having well-researched, accurate information on endometriosis that we deliver with a sense of humor! Our goal is to help others feel supported, inspired, and more empowered on their own health journeys.

Above all, I'm sending you support and wishing you many symptom-free days.

instagram.com/in16yearsofendo
facebook.com/amy.corfeli

NOTES

Introduction to Endometriosis

1. Osborne, Hannah. "Here Are 20 of the Most Painful Health Conditions You Can Get." *Newsweek*, 10 October 2018, https://www.newsweek.com/20-most-painful-conditions-nhs-1191081
2. Arrington, J. "The Standard of Care is Not Sufficient!" NancysNookEndo, https://nancysnookendo.com/learning-library/treatment/lessons/the-standard-of-care-is-not-sufficient-by-dr-arrington/

My Endometriosis Story

1. Excision surgery is a technique which removes endometriosis at the root. This is different from ablation surgery, which only superficially burns the surface of the endometriosis, leaving the root behind.

Is Endometriosis a 'Devastating Disease'?

1. I've used this more inclusive spelling of the word 'women' to recognize that not everyone who is assigned female at birth identifies as a woman.

11. Get Well Soon

1. The ovaries and uterus are not the only places that endometriosis can present, but many gynecologists who lack training and experience with endometriosis are unaware that endometriosis can be found anywhere throughout the pelvic region, such as on the bowels and bladder.
2. The visual appearance of endometriosis and its impact on our concepts of the disease. http://endopaedia.info/origin32.html

15. Untangling Myself from My Thoughts

1. Gustafson C. Bruce Lipton, PhD: The Jump From Cell Culture to Consciousness. Integr Med (Encinitas). 2017 Dec;16(6):44-50. PMID: 30936816; PMCID: PMC6438088.

16. No More Options

1. At that time, I was nineteen years old and didn't know that there were indeed more options for managing symptoms. That was all *this* doctor could offer me, but there were more options such as diet and lifestyle changes, acupuncture, or Traditional Chinese Medicine. Since I wasn't yet diagnosed with endometriosis, I wasn't aware of excision surgery or that I could seek treatment with a doctor more experienced in endometriosis.

24. A Lucky Coincidence

1. Diet and lifestyle changes cannot cure endometriosis or prevent the disease from progressing, but it may help a person manage their symptoms. Diet and lifestyle changes are individual and what works for one person may not work for another.

29. What is Life Asking of Me?

1. I've used this more inclusive spelling of the word 'women' to recognize that not everyone who is assigned female at birth identifies as a woman.

32. The Mighty Oak Inside of Us

1. These are 10-day silent meditation retreats that are run on donations. Vipassana is a secular meditation technique that teaches self-observation and awareness. It focuses on the interconnection between the mind and body, training a person to sit with the sensations in their body to gain insight into themselves. For more information or to sign up for a retreat, visit https://www.dhamma.org/

33. A Lifeboat in a Storm of Emotions

1. I'm referring to my own passing emotions here, such as sadness, anger, shame, frustration, helplessness, disappointment, and vulnerability, and not states such as trauma, grief, clinical depression, or anxiety disorder. It is recommended to reach out to a mental health professional for support with these states, for emotions that feel unsafe to sit with, if you have lingering emotions that do not pass, or for any other situation in which you feel like you need extra support to be with certain emotions.

42. Is Happiness Possible?

1. I'm not referring here to clinical depression and other mental health conditions. If you suspect you are clinically depressed or have another mental health condition, it's recommended to seek help from a mental health professional.

48. I Can Handle What I Feel

1. Important—here I am referring to *my* own passing feelings. If you have suicidal ideations, thoughts, or urges, please reach out for help right away to a national suicide prevention hotline, a qualified mental health professional, or a loved one.
2. I'm referring to passing emotions here, not states such as trauma, grief, clinical depression, or anxiety disorder. It is recommended to reach out to a mental health professional for support with these or if you have lingering emotions that do not pass.

50. The Wisdom of a Butterfly

1. One name for a group of butterflies flying together is a kaleidoscope.

52. The Infuriating Flower

1. I was unaware at the time, but a hysterectomy does not cure endometriosis. This is a common myth with endometriosis.

57. I Won't Live in Fear Anymore

1. When working with fear (especially if from a trauma), many people benefit from enlisting the support of a mental health professional.

60. My Pain Was Always Real

1. I have listed some resources on my website www.insixteenyears.com

70. A Cruel Twist of Fate

1. Excision surgery is a technique which removes endometriosis at the root. This is different from ablation surgery, which only superficially burns the surface of the endometriosis, often leaving the root behind.
2. Histamine intolerance can occur when a person has an overload of histamine in the body and the body is unable to break it all down. Histamine is found in varying levels in foods, and many activities and chemicals can trigger a histamine release. Mast cell activation syndrome is when mast cells, which are involved in the body's allergy response, are overactive and release inflammatory molecules at inappropriate times.

ACKNOWLEDGMENTS

To my sister and to my best friend,

This book wouldn't have been possible if it wasn't for you both.

Thank you, Susan, for the hundreds of hours (thousands?! Quite possibly!) you spent editing this book, for your war on the word 'things', and for teaching me grammar rules like how to correctly use a comma. You edited this book even when your own life was busy and demanding, and I cannot thank you enough.

Thank you, Brittany, for your genius idea to add self-reflections to the book, for reassuring me during my moments of self-doubt, and for understanding me on such a deep level. You sit with me every week in our podcast box, and those hours of conversation inspired many of the topics in this book.

Made in the USA
Middletown, DE
23 February 2021

34306521R00198